# OUR EARTH

*by* ARTHUR BEISER

PHYSICS FOR EVERYBODY
GUIDE TO THE MICROSCOPE
OUR EARTH

# OUR EARTH

The properties of our planet, how they were
discovered, and how they came into being

· BY ARTHUR BEISER

**ILLUSTRATED**

**E. P. DUTTON & CO., INC.**
*New York 1959*

# Contents

# List of Illustrations

*Following page 64*

# OUR EARTH

# Preface

THERE ARE FASHIONS IN SCIENCE AS IN MOST OF MAN'S ACTIVI-
ties, and they share the same lack of logic. How else to explain why we know more about the interior of the atom than
about the interior of the earth? In the past few years, though,
the once dowdy subject of geophysics has been found to possess style and elegance after all, and today the earth, its properties, and its strange and violent history find themselves
under the inquisitive gaze of the scientist to an unprece-
dented degree.

The last two thousand years or so have seen, it is true, a
large body of facts, theories, and speculation accumulate
about the earth. But we are still a long way from a complete
picture of our planet. Balancing our knowledge of the mountain building and erosion processes that created the topography of the continents is our ignorance of the origin of the
continents themselves. We have some understanding of volcanos and earthquakes—but we are aware of little more about
the molten iron heart deep within the earth than its existence.

The International Geophysical Year program was set up
in an effort to learn more about the earth, from its very cen-

ter to the outer reaches of its atmosphere. This program, which was carried on during the eighteen months from July, 1957, through December, 1958, was a great success, providing an anomalous example of international cooperation as well as supplying the science of geophysics with a huge collection of data. Right now the analysis of the data is under way, an endeavor whose end is many years in the future.

Today there is a quality of excitement, the thrill of a chase still in progress, about geophysics. The earth has turned out to be a fascinating object in its own right besides being our dwelling place. In writing this book I have tried to convey some of this sense of intellectual adventure. Much of the material I discuss is generally accepted by the scientific community; but I have not avoided subjects, such as the changing length of the day, whose status is neither certain nor likely to become so for some time. Through my association with the International Geophysical Year I have had access to many of its results, of which I have made use wherever possible.

The stimulating thing about science is the feeling its practitioners have of being on the frontier of knowledge, a feeling which I hope comes through in the pages that follow.

A. B.

*New York University*

# ONE

# The Dimensions of the World

As far back in the remote past as scholars have been able to penetrate, evidence of scientific activity has been found. Not, to be sure, science as we know it, with its insistence upon empirical support for every hypothesis and its emphasis on causality and logical structure, but nevertheless a recognizable ancestor of modern science. The science of antiquity had a number of triumphs, several of which we shall explore, although its far-fetched speculations are perhaps better known.

Few subjects intrigued the imagination of the ancients more than the earth and its position in the universe. For example, the Egyptian civilization visualized the universe as a great box, with Egypt in the center of its long, narrow, floor. The top of the box is the sky, from which lamps are suspended by means of ropes. These lamps are the stars. Other lamps, carried in heavenly boats, travel about the sky and appear as planets. The Milky Way was supposed to be the celestial equivalent of the Nile, and the regions through which it flowed were populated with dead Egyptians dwelling under the benign supervision of Osiris.

At the corners of the universe-box are four huge mountains supporting the sky, and joining them around the sides of the box are mountain ranges. Along these mountains a river circumscribes the universe. In this river each morning, in the east, the sun-god Ra is reborn in a boat, appearing as a ball of fire. As the boat proceeds along the river Ra grows and waxes bright, until at noon he has achieved his full splendor. Then he transfers to another boat, and continues along the river to the valley of Dait. Dait is in perpetual night, and in order to transit it the declining Ra changes to a succession of other boats. Now and then a serpent attacks Ra and briefly obscures his brilliance, an event corresponding to a solar eclipse. The sun seems higher in the summer because the river overflows its banks in that season, just as its branch the Nile does, and the craft transporting Ra is therefore able to approach closer to Egypt.

In the same river there is another boat that carries the moon. Each month a sow attacks the moon, and after two weeks of struggle succeeds in destroying it. As soon as this has happened the moon is reborn, with another two weeks required for it to mature. At times the celestial sow is able to devour the moon entirely, a catastrophe observed as a lunar eclipse.

The early Greeks were more prosaic. Three thousand years ago they pictured the earth as a kind of saucer surrounded by the river Okeanos. The sun, moon, and stars rise from Okeanos in the east and fall into it in the west. We do not know how the heavenly bodies were supposed to be transported around to the east during the night, but they cannot go underneath the earth since that region, Tartarus, never sees the sun. Erebus, where the dead dwell, extends out from Okeanos to the west of the Earth, with a fog preventing the rays of the setting sun from reaching it.

More elaborate versions of this conception were formulated later. The earth and heavens rose from Chaos, a region between the bottom of the earth and Tartarus. The source of Okeanos lies in the West (that is, in the Atlantic Ocean), and a branch of it, the Styx, goes underground to Hades. The stars are nailed to the sky, which is made of a solid material like crystal. The firmament revolves around the earth "like a hat around the head."

\* \* \*

And so on and on went the embroidery of the mind. But even as the fancies of the philosophers multiplied and convoluted, various observations began to be pieced together to give what was in some respects a remarkably accurate picture of the earth and the solar system. As early as the fifth century B.C., Parmenides of Elea declared that the earth is a sphere. If we are charitable we shall ascribe his finding to an analysis of the tales of travelers, who discovered that when they went north a greater number of stars remained above the horizon all night, while when they went south additional stars became visible (for instance Canopus, unseen in Greece, just visible at Rhodes, and prominent in the sky farther south). The early travelers also reported that the length of the day changes with what we call latitude, a rather difficult fact to explain in terms of a flat earth. (If we are not charitable, on the other hand, we can attribute Parmenides' statement to the same vague intuitions that led him to the belief that everything which exists is ultimately composed of spherical components.)

Another major Greek figure sometimes credited with teaching that the earth is a globe is Pythagoras. There is no doubt that the school he founded, which flourished for two hundred years, ultimately adopted this view, but because of the tendency of his successors to attribute all discoveries to

13

their master it is by no means certain that Pythagoras himself held to the sphericity of the earth. The Pythagoreans, for a time, were about the only ones to have faith in this idea, and they went on to develop an impressively ingenious, though quite incorrect, theory of the universe.

In time, as the notion that the earth is round became accepted in ancient Greece, attempts were made to estimate its size. Aristotle quotes 400,000 stadia for the circumference, much too big, without stating the source of this figure, which was probably obtained from the work of the earlier and highly talented mathematician and astronomer Eudoxus. Archimedes, also omitting references, later gave the circumference as 300,000 stadia, which is better though still 20 per cent in error.

The best of the early measurements of the earth's circumference was made by Eratosthenes (276-194 B.C.), who spent the latter half of his life in charge of the great library at Alexandria. He knew that at Syene, which was due south of Alexandria, the sun was directly overhead at noon on the first day of summer. On the first day of summer in 250 B.C. he carefully measured the extent to which the sun's rays slanted away from the vertical at noon in Alexandria, an angle he found to be 1/50 of a complete circle or a little over 7°. Since the distance from Syene to Alexandria was 5000 stadia, the circumference of the earth, corresponding to a full circle of 360°, must be 50 times 5000, or 250,000 stadia. How long is a stadium? There were several different ones in use in the ancient world, but it seems likely that Eratosthenes used the stadium of 517 feet which the professional pacers of the time employed in surveying distances. This means a circumference of 24,500 miles, not far from the 24,860 mile meridional circumference of more recent determinations.

Eratosthenes, or some follower of his, then felt that it would be very elegant to have the length equivalent of each degree of latitude equal a round number, and he accordingly set this number at 700 stadia. The final value of the circumference thus became 360 times 700, or 252,000 stadia, about 24,660 miles—less than a per cent away from the true figure, but testimony more to luck than to skill.

\* \* \*

While the earth is certainly more nearly round than any other shape, it is not a perfect sphere. This was predicted by Newton, who reasoned that, since the earth is spinning rapidly on its axis, the equatorial portions should experience a greater centrifugal force than the polar ones. At the equator itself, the centrifugal force on an object is about 1/300 of the gravitational force on it. As a result the earth must bulge slightly on the equator and be slightly flattened at the poles, much like a grapefruit. Newton's analysis was, however, disputed by the astronomers Cassini, a father and son with whose name is associated the first accurate measurement of the distance from the earth to the sun, the division between the outer and middle rings of Saturn, and some rather ill-founded notions regarding planetary orbits. The Cassinis felt that the earth was elongated at the poles, something like a football.

In order to settle the question, Louis XV financed a pair of expeditions in 1736. In one Pierre-Louis de Maupertuis went to Lapland to measure the precise length of a degree of latitude, while in the other La Condamine went to the equator to perform a similar determination there. The results vindicated Newton, and Maupertuis, who as a champion of Newton was the prime mover in the affair, was said to have simultaneously flattened both the earth and the Cassinis. Maupertuis, already a mathematician of note, went on to do prophetic work in physics, biology, and philosophy, although at the time he seems to have been noted as much for bringing back with him a pair of diminutive Lapp ladies as for his scientific achievement. (One of them ended up in a convent and the other was later unhappily married.)

More recent determinations of the length of a degree of latitude yield 68.70 miles at the equator and 68.41 miles at the poles—which works out to the conclusion that the earth is a bit over 13 miles wider than it is high. The earth's centrifugal distortion, as it is called, amounts to 0.34 per cent; by comparison, the distortion of Mars is 0.53 per cent, of Jupiter 6.2 per cent, of Saturn 9.6 per cent, of Uranus 6 per cent, and of Neptune 2 per cent. Mercury and Venus, which turn slowly on their axes, have no measurable flattening, while Pluto is too small and far away for anybody to tell. The moon is less than a mile away from being a perfect sphere, which, in terms of its size, means that the moon is slightly more distorted than the earth.

\* \* \*

The over-all flattening of the earth is not the only deviation in its shape from a perfect sphere. Our poor planet is also warped and dented, and on top of this its skin is wrinkled into mountains and valleys both above and below sea level. Still, while the earth is a pretty irregular object as seen by man, viewed from outside it would seem smoother than the finest billiard ball. The total range from the Pacific depths to the summit of Everest is only a little over 12 miles, which is less than one-third of a per cent of the earth's 4000-mile radius.

There are three widely used models of the earth's shape. These are illustrated in Figure 1. The first is the sphere, but for a great many scientific purposes it is not adequate. Next is the oblate spheroid which incorporates the polar flattening predicted by Newton. This is the form the earth would have if there were no irregularities in its internal structure. The "standard earth" was computed in terms of an oblate spheroid by J. F. Hayford in 1910, and the dimensions of the Hayford spheroid, as it has become known, are those of the regular geometric form which is closest to the contours of the actual earth.

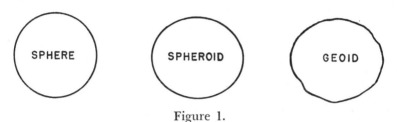

Figure 1.

The next approximation to the configuration of the earth is the geoid. The geoid mirrors the bulges and indentations that are averaged out in the Hayford spheroid, while it ignores such small-scale irregularities as mountains. In essence the geoid is the sea-level equivalent earth; a plumb line suspended anywhere on the geoid would always hang perpendicular to its surface, which is not true of the idealized Hayford spheroid or, for that matter, of the actual earth.

Over a hundred years ago Sir George Stokes pointed out that the geoid could be determined on the basis of gravity measurements made all over the world. Today the art of evaluating the force of gravity in terms of the acceleration $g$ it imparts to free-falling bodies is highly developed, and exceedingly precise gravimeters have been built that make use of either a vibrating spring or an oscillating pendulum. The ancestor of these gravimeters was a beautiful pendulum clock built in Paris in the mid-eighteenth century for an astronomical observatory in French Guiana. It was accurate

enough in Paris, but when transported to Guiana it proceeded to lose $2\frac{1}{2}$ minutes per day. Brought back to Paris,
the clock kept perfect time once more. Now when the theory
of the pendulum is worked out, the formula for the period
$T$ of its bob (that is, the time required for a complete swing)
turns out to be $T = 2\pi\sqrt{L/g}$, where $L$ is the length of the
pendulum and $g$ the acceleration caused by gravity. (This
formula, strictly speaking, applies only to an ideal pendulum,
and it must be modified slightly in the case of actual pendu-
lums.) Since $g$—which averages about 32.2 ft/sec²—is propor-
tional to the force of gravity at the point where it is
measured, the variation in the accuracy of the clock could be
interpreted as arising from differences in the force of gravity
between Paris and French Guiana. Pierre Bouguer made this
suggestion, and with the help of a fairly crude apparatus
made a pioneer series of gravimetric determinations.

How can gravity measurements yield the shape of the
geoid? The answer is that if we are far from the center of
the earth on the crest of a bulge, the force of attraction is
weak, while if we are in a depression the attractive force is
greater than at the "normal" surface. (Of course, if we de-
scend into the earth's interior in a deep hole, the gravitational force will diminish until it is zero at the center.
However, the force is actually larger than usual if we are on
the earth's surface in a dent, so to speak, since then we are
closer to the bulk of the mass of the earth without having any
above us.) Means have been devised to take into account the
effects on gravity of local anomalies, such as mineral deposits,
which would otherwise make it impossible to evaluate the
geoid.

The best modern instruments can measure gravity in ab-
solute terms with an accuracy of one part in two hundred
thousand, while comparisons can be made to about one part

in a billion. The two big difficulties in surveying the earth's gravity are the enormous area that is involved, nearly two hundred million square miles, and the fact that most of this area is covered by water, making it impossible to use ordinary gravimeters, whose primary requirement is a firm base. The solution to the first difficulty is a comprehensive international effort, and the IGY program seems to be a start in this direction.

The other trouble is more complicated. It is not hard to make a gravimeter which can be enclosed in a watertight box and lowered to the ocean floor, either recording the data there or transmitting them to its parent ship electrically. Unfortunately this strategem can only be used in the minor part of the oceans in which the depth is not prohibitively great. Thirty years ago F. A. Vening Meinesz of Holland developed a gravimeter that could be used on the spongy terrain of his country, and it soon developed that the same instrument could be successfully employed on a submerged submarine. The big advantage of a submerged submarine is that it is free from the continual rocking and pitching of a surface ship, and the Meinesz gravimeter was able to correct for the submarine's more gentle motions. Up to the end of World War II, 1200 measurements of gravity at sea were made, nearly all by Meinesz. Since then American, British, and Dutch scientists have made an additional 4000 determinations with the help of submarines. Very recently a gravimeter has been perfected which can be used on surface ships, a notable step forward since it renders accessible to geophysicists the 80 per cent of the earth's surface under water. This device requires a gyrostabilized platform, hardly a common item, and only preliminary tests have been made thus far with it, but it seems probable that it will be a success. If so, the way will have been paved for an immense increase in our knowledge of the shape of the earth and the manner in which its mass is distributed.

\* \* \*

It is possible to turn the pages of a reference handbook and find there the statement that the earth weighs 6,595,000,000,-000,000,000,000 tons, give or take a billion billion tons or so. To someone not acquainted with the indirect methods of science this must seem a preposterous assertion, particularly since it implies that the density of the earth as a whole is twice that of any of the materials of which its surface is composed. Yet there is no dispute about this figure in the scientific community, and in fact it is one of the more secure aspects of our knowledge of our planet.

Isaac Newton, that giant in the history of science, was the first to suggest a method for finding the mass of the earth. We cannot bring up his name a second time without noting his extraordinary life. Newton was born in 1642, the year of Galileo's death, and had an unremarkable childhood. In 1665 an outbreak of plague closed Cambridge University, at which young Newton was studying, whereupon he returned to his mother's farm in rural Woolsthorpe where the absence of other diversions turned his mind to contemplating the universe. In short order Newton, all of twenty-three, had invented the binomial theorem and calculus, discovered the three fundamental laws governing the motion of bodies, formulated the law of gravitation and deduced from it Kepler's empirical laws of planetary motion, and conducted optical experiments of a high order. An achievement with no equal, made by a man who, still brilliant but with ardor gone, later spent half of his adult life as Master of the Mint where he divided his time between supervising the coinage of Britain (for a commission) and investigating rather absurd theological problems.

Newton's idea was this. When we suspend an object from a string, it ideally hangs "straight down"—meaning that it points toward the center of the earth. However, if there is a mountain nearby, the gravitational pull of the mountain causes the plumb bob to be deflected from the vertical (Figure 2). The precise amount of the deflection is a measure

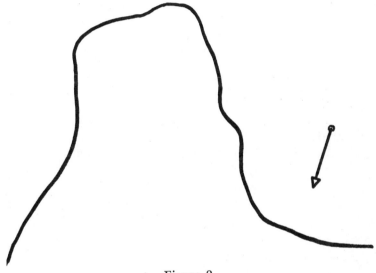

Figure 2.

of the ratio between the mountain's mass and the mass of the rest of the earth. Finding the mass of the mountain is, in theory, a simple matter: first determine its volume, an elementary problem in surveying, and then multiply by the density of the rock of which it is made. Since density is mass per unit volume, this gives the required number, and from the angle made by the plumb bob the earth's mass can then be computed.

21

In 1738, eleven years after Newton's death, Pierre Bouguer carried out an experiment of this kind. It is evident that the larger the mountain, the more the deflection and hence the greater the accuracy. Bouguer went to Mt. Chimborazo, in what is now Ecuador, whose 20,640 foot elevation is indicative of its enormous size. His data were not especially good, however, partly because of uncertainty in the mass of the mountain and partly because of the crude nature of his instruments, but at least he was able to establish that the earth's interior was neither empty nor filled with water, as certain of his contemporaries believed.

The next attempt was made in 1776 by Maskelyne, then Astronomer Royal, in Scotland. His estimate for the earth's weight was $5.4 \times 10^{21}$ tons, which was later raised to $6.0 \times 10^{21}$ tons when the mass of the mountain (Schiehallion) was ascertained more precisely. (The quantity $10^{21}$ is mathematical shorthand for 1 followed by 21 zeros: thus $5.4 \times 10^{21}$ is 5,400,000,000,000,000,000,000 when written out.) The latter figure is not too far away from the current value of $6.595 \times 10^{21}$ tons, which is remarkable in view of the approximate nature of the entire experiment.

\*   \*   \*

A much better method was proposed by John Michell. He started from Newton's law of gravitation which states that the force $F$ between two bodies of masses $m$ and $M$ respectively whose centers are separated by the distance $r$ is

$$F = G\frac{mM}{r^2} \quad ,$$

where $G$ is a universal constant of nature. In other words, the heavier bodies and the closer together they are, the greater will be the gravitational attraction between them.

22

At the surface of the earth, the gravitational force (which is manifested as weight) on a mass $m$ is therefore given by

$$F = G \frac{mM_{earth}}{r^2_{earth}} \quad .$$

According to the Second Law of Motion, the relationship between the force on a body of mass $m$ and its resulting acceleration $a$ is $F = m\,a$. Near the earth, as Galileo discovered, *all* objects fall with the same acceleration of 32.2 feet/second² (neglecting the effects of air resistance), usually denoted, as we know, by $g$. If we equate these two expressions for the force exerted by the earth on a body at its surface, we find that

$$\frac{G\,mM_{earth}}{r^2_{earth}} = mg$$

or

$$M_{earth} = \frac{gr^2_{earth}}{G} \quad .$$

We already know the precise figures for both $g$ and $r_{earth}$, and so if we can only evaluate $G$, the constant of gravitation, we shall be able to obtain the mass of the earth at once.

Michell even proposed a means for determining $G$. He invented an especially sensitive form of a balance, called a torsion balance, to measure the force of attraction between two small spheres attached to the ends of a suspended rod and two larger stationary spheres (Figure 3). By first calibrating the suspension wire so that the amount of force needed to twist it by a unit amount is known, the deflection that results when the large spheres are brought up can be converted to the force value involved. This measurement was carried out by Michell's friend Henry Cavendish in 1798, who ob-

23

tained a result not far from the currently accepted one. (Cavendish, who inherited a vast fortune but devoted himself exclusively to science, used a similar balance in studying the forces exerted by electrical charges on one another; he also did notable work in the chemistry of gases.)

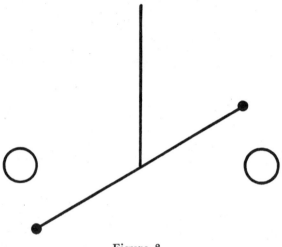

Figure 3.

A perhaps still more direct experiment was made later by Jolly, who simply weighed a few pounds of mercury carefully, and then measured the increase in the weight of the mercury when six tons of lead were placed directly below it. However, the Cavendish method is the superior one in practice, and figured in the most recent (1930) determination of G at the National Bureau of Standards in Washington. In the latter 1½ ounce gold spheres were placed at the ends of an 8-inch rod, and the external masses were in the form of steel cylinders weighing 145 pounds each. In the absence of the cylinders the rod required about 30 minutes to swing back and forth when displaced slightly; when the cylinders were put in place, the period of vibration was reduced by the gravitational attraction between them and the spheres to about 25 minutes, and from this difference $G$ could be calculated with great accuracy.

# TWO

# The Solar System

THE SOLAR SYSTEM IS FAR FROM BEING A CASUAL COLLECTION of objects in thrall to the sun. The planets behave in a most orderly fashion in their courses, and the discovery of the regularities they exhibit has had striking consequences in all realms of human thought.

From the very beginning, it was man's fancy to think of his home as the very center of the universe. To the primitive mind it was obvious that the earth is stationary and that the sun, moon, planets, and stars revolve about it. Then, with the growth of religions having anthropomorphic deities, theological as well as common-sense objections could be raised against any attempt to displace the earth from its cardinality. A subordinate role for the earth threatened the cosmic status of the medieval Church, whose riposte to this and other heretical ideas—however well founded—was the auto-da-fé. So resourceful a Church found it possible to postpone officially acknowledging the sun as the center of the solar system until 1822.

Perhaps the first correct public statement of the arrangement of the solar system was made by Aristarchus (310-230

26

B.C.), who believed that "the fixed stars and the sun remain unmoved, that the earth revolves round the sun on the circumference of a circle, the sun lying at the center of the orbit." Never popular, this idea was soon discarded in favor of the complex but apparently successful theory of Hipparchus. Hipparchus placed the earth in the center of the

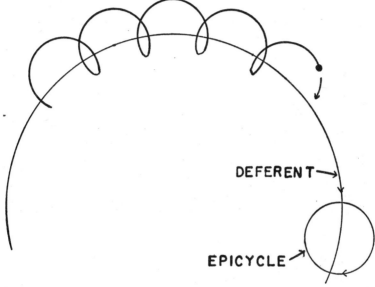

Figure 4.

universe, with the sun, moon, and planets traveling around it in the manner shown in Figure 4. These peculiar paths are made up of two simple motions superimposed: the body's revolution in a small circle called an epicycle, and the revolution of the center of the epicycle in a larger circle, called the deferent, about the earth. Ptolemy, in the second century A.D., incorporated the deferent-epicycle explanation of the

27

movements of the heavenly bodies into his Almagest, a compendium of Astronomy which was to remain the standard reference on the subject for over a thousand years. (The Arabs, custodians of ancient mathematics and science, considered the work the "greatest of books" and Almagest is a contraction of this phrase.)

Unfortunately the combination of two circular motions per body did not accord precisely with observational data, with the result that the original twelve motions—one each for the sun and moon, two each for Mercury, Venus, Mars, Jupiter, and Saturn—multiplied until seventy different motions were required. The great beauty of Hipparchus' plan lay in its simplicity, but in time the geocentric system became less and less elegant as it was patched up to fit successively more accurate measurements. One of Copernicus' arguments against the Ptolemaic system, in fact, was that it failed to be "sufficiently pleasing to the mind."

One of the reasons for the disregard of Aristarchus' model of the solar system was his failure to elaborate it in a quantitative way. Copernicus (1473-1543), in taking over his concept, made it into a detailed scheme of the heavens: "Of the moving bodies first comes Saturn, who completes his circuit in thirty years. After him Jupiter, moving in a twelve year revolution. Then Mars, who revolves biennially. Fourth in order an annual cycle takes place, in which we have said is contained the Earth, with the lunar orbit as an epicycle, that is, with the moon moving in a circle about the earth. In the fifth place Venus is carried around in nine months. Then Mercury holds the sixth place, circulating in the space of eighty days. In the middle of all dwells the Sun. Who indeed in this most beautiful temple would place the torch in any other or better place than one whence it can illuminate the whole at the same time?"

In all honesty, we must admit that Copernicus' work was

no more accurate in predicting planetary motions than that of his predecessors. And the neat picture of the solar system as a series of circular orbits about a fixed sun, so gratifying esthetically, was equally displeasing to the ego as well as being "altogether opposed to the Holy Scriptures." It is not until we come to Kepler and Newton that the heliocentric view becomes impossible to refute.

*　*　*

The latter half of the sixteenth century saw the first significant improvement in astronomical measurements since the time of the Greeks. Tycho Brahe, a Dane, perceived that the measurements of planetary motions then in existence were not particularly accurate, and he had built for himself an observatory at the Castle of Benatky whose instruments were as rigid and precise as possible. With the help of these instruments Tycho, blessed with exceptional eyesight and perspicuity, made thousands of measurements, a labor that occupied most of his life. Even without the telescope, which had not yet been invented, Tycho's observatory was able to determine celestial angles to better than 1/100 of a degree.

At his death in 1601 Tycho left behind him his own somewhat peculiar theory of the solar system, a body of superb data extending over many years, and an assistant named Johannes Kepler. Kepler regarded the Copernican scheme "with incredible and ravishing delight," and fully expected that Tycho's improved figures would prove Copernicus right once and for all. But this was not the case; after four years of work on the orbit of Mars alone, Kepler could not reconcile the observational data with any of the models of the solar system that had by then been proposed. If the facts do not agree with the theory, then the theory, no matter how attractive, must be discarded. Kepler began a search for

29

a new cosmic design that would accord with Tycho's observations.

After considering every possibility, which meant years of drudgery in performing calculations by hand, Kepler found that circular orbits for the planets were out of the question even when modified in various plausible ways. Discarding the circle led to other geometrical figures being considered, and here Kepler found the truth: the planetary orbits are ellipses with the sun at one focus (Figure 5).

Figure 5.

This epochal discovery was not sufficient, as Kepler realized, for the virtue of the older schemes was that they could be used to predict—with adequate accuracy for most purposes—the course of the planets through the sky. What was needed now was a law that would relate the speeds of the planets to their positions in their elliptical orbits. Kepler could not be sure that such a law even existed, and he was in "ecstasy" when he came upon the answer: the planets move so that their radius vectors (which are imaginary lines drawn from the sun to the planets) sweep out equal areas in equal times. Thus, in Figure 5, each of the shaded areas is covered in the same period of time, which means that the planets travel more rapidly when they are near the sun (perihelion) than when they are far from the sun (aphelion). The earth, for instance, has a speed of 18.8 miles/second at perihelion and 18.2 miles/second at aphelion, a difference of over 3 per cent.

A great achievement, but Kepler was not satisfied. He was

obsessed with the idea of order and regularity in the universe, and the idea that the courses of the planets are not manifestations of some general pattern seemed incredible to him. So Kepler persevered, and after ten years could announce the discovery of the harmonic law of planetary motion: the ratio between the square of the time $T$ required by a planet to make a complete revolution around the sun and the cube of its average distance $R$ from the sun is a constant for *all* the planets. That is, $T^2/R^3$ has the same value throughout the solar system, and Kepler had accomplished his dream of linking the planets.

Kepler had less success in trying to fathom the causes of his laws of planetary motion, though he had a clear idea of what he was after: "My aim in this is to show that the celestial machine is to be likened not to a divine organism but rather to a clockwork." It was left to Newton, a half century later, to find that the same laws of nature apply in the universe as are valid on the surface of the earth, and that the gravitational force that attracts apples to the ground is identical with the gravitational force that keeps the planets in their orbits about the sun—a hardly self-evident concept. Newton did more than merely explain Kepler's discovery of elliptical orbits, the law of equal areas, and the harmonic law; he showed that these features of the solar system are absolutely inevitable consequences of natural laws, thereby demonstrating a much more profound kind of order in the universe than his predecessors had conceived.

\* \* \*

Perhaps the most sought-for regularity in the solar system is one relating the distances of the planets from the sun. Kepler thought he had found the answer when he noticed that, if a cube were placed inside a sphere the radius of the

31

orbit of Saturn, a sphere inscribed within the cube had almost the identical radius as Jupiter's orbit. A tetrahedron inscribed in Jupiter's sphere will just enclose a sphere whose radius is that of the orbit of Mars; and so on, with the five regular solids interposed between spheres representing the orbits of the six planets known at the time. This celestial model gave Kepler more joy than any of his other discoveries, but its imprecision and the finding of additional planets which cannot be fitted into the model make it impossible for us to share his pleasure.

Some two hundred years later an equally odd—even astrological—relationship turned up which has lost neither validity nor inexplicability. It is so well established that some astrophysicists have designed theories of the origin of the solar system primarily to account for it, while others prefer to pretend that it is really not there at all, in order to avoid contradiction. This rule, known as Bode's law after its finder, states that the distance from the sun of any planet, counting the earth's distance from the sun as 1, may be found by taking the number 0.4 and adding to it 0 for Mercury, 0.3 for Venus, 0.6 for the Earth, 1.2 for Mars, and so on, doubling the number to be added to the constant 0.4 for each successive planet. The result is a table of planetary distance such as the following:

| PLANET | PREDICTED DISTANCE | ACTUAL DISTANCE |
|---|---|---|
| Mercury | 0.4 + 0.0 = 0.4 | 0.387 |
| Venus | 0.4 + 0.3 = 0.7 | 0.723 |
| Earth | 0.4 + 0.6 = 1.0 | 1.000 |
| Mars | 0.4 + 1.2 = 1.6 | 1.524 |
| Asteroids | 0.4 + 2.4 = 2.8 | 2.9 (average) |
| Jupiter | 0.4 + 4.8 = 5.2 | 5.203 |
| Saturn | 0.4 + 9.6 = 10.0 | 9.546 |
| Uranus | 0.4 + 19.2 = 19.6 | 19.20 |
| Neptune | 0.4 + 38.4 = 38.8 | 30.09 |
| Pluto | 0.4 + 76.8 = 77.2 | 39.5 |

Evidently Bode's law is quite accurate out to Uranus, is rather poor for Neptune, and is hopeless for Pluto. (It is only fair to note that Pluto has certain anomalous properties, such as the 17° inclination of its orbit to the plane containing the orbits of all the other planets, that make it unlikely that Pluto shared the origin of the rest of the solar system.) In Bode's time the asteroids, Uranus, Neptune, and Pluto were still unknown; Bode had no reason to suppose that planets beyond Saturn existed, but he felt strongly about the apparent gap between Mars and Jupiter— "Can we believe that the Creator of the world has left this space empty? Certainly not!"

The first confirmation of Bode's law came unexpectedly with Herschel's discovery of Uranus, which fitted almost perfectly into the table after Saturn. Evidently this was no fortuitous relationship, but one to be taken seriously. The search for the missing planet began in earnest, and soon Piazzi, a Sicilian astronomer, found a tiny object in almost exactly the right place—Ceres, about 460 miles across. Shortly afterward a number of other minor planets, now called asteroids, were found which infest the region between Mars and Jupiter. Their average distance from the sun is 2.9 times the earth's distance, almost exactly as predicted by Bode's law. Of the over 1500 asteroids whose properties are known (there are thousands more), the great majority are between 10 and 50 miles across; their total mass is a good bit less than that of the moon. The asteroids almost certainly are either the remnants of a planetary gestation somehow aborted, or, possibly, the fragments of a shattered planet.

In fact, as additional evidence for order in the solar system, formulas mathematically identical with Bode's law predict the distances of the eleven satellites of Jupiter, the nine satellites of Saturn, and the four satellites of Uranus from their respective parent planets with an error seldom exceeding 5 per cent. A satisfying symmetry, but as yet no Newton has come upon the scene to transmute it into meaning.

* * *

While we are on the subject of the earth in space, it seems appropriate to look into a related subject that is, for most of us, at least as interesting as the organization of the heavens. Is there life on other worlds? Indeed, are there any other "worlds" that deserve the name?

Estimating the number of planets throughout the universe that are presently supporting life of some sort is a favorite sport of astronomers. Harlow Shapley goes about it in a very general way. He starts with the estimate that a single star out of every million has a family of planets accompanying it —a most conservative figure, since most hypotheses of planetary origin suggest that planetary systems occur naturally in the evolution of nearly all stars save double ones. Next, Shapley supposes that only one of each thousand of these systems has "a planet with the happy requirements of suitable distance from the star, near-circular orbit, proper mass, salubrious atmosphere, and reasonable rotation period—all of which are necessary for life as we know it on earth." A billion stars, therefore are needed to provide a planet like ours. Even then we cannot take for granted that life will have come into being. Shall we say that the chances are 999 to 1 against this? Now we must comb a trillion stars before we can find one which has a life-bearing world whirling round it. But there are more than a hundred billion billion stars in the universe, how many more we do not know. Even this figure, though, means that the rock-bottom minimum number of planets in existence that resemble the earth even to bearing living creatures (many, no doubt, vastly superior to Homo sapiens) is one hundred million.

Otto Struve approaches the problem in a slightly different manner. He notes that only about 10 per cent of the stars in our galaxy (the Milky Way) rotate slowly, taking weeks to turn once on their axes. The others are spinning much faster. Now the reason that the sun requires about 28 days for each rotation is that almost all of the angular momentum of the solar system is concentrated in the planets, with the sun possessing less than 1 per cent of the total (see Chapter 7). A reasonable conclusion is that the stars that turn slowly do so because they are accompanied by swarms of planets which share their angular momenta. With a hundred billion stars in the galaxy, this means that ten billion have planetary systems; if these have an average of five planets each, there is a total of fifty billion planets in our galaxy alone. Struve thinks that perhaps one in fifty can support life of some sort, and that between one in a hundred and one in a thousand of those capable of maintaining life have evolved creatures as intelligent as man. A total, then, of over a million inhabited planets in our galaxy alone, and, if the other galaxies are similar, many billions throughout the universe. Struve's figures differ from those of Shapley, but the basic point is inescapable: we are not alone.

A skeptic may inquire why, if indeed there is so immense a number of planets bearing sentient life, we have no direct knowledge of such life—no mysterious messages in broken English, no space ships alighting with little green men inside. Much of the reason is surely the combination of the immense distances between the stars and the impossibility of achieving speeds faster than that of light, which would offer the potentiality of bridging such distances in a reasonable number of lifetimes. And it is also conceivable that there is some kind of limit to the ultimate intelligence life can achieve. Perhaps, as Struve suggests, this limit may reveal itself in explosions of supernovae, those cosmic catastrophes which occur every couple of hundred years or so. "It is perfectly conceivable that some intelligent race meddled once too often with nuclear laws and blew themselves to bits."

# THREE

# Within the Earth

EVER SINCE IT WAS DISCOVERED THAT THE OVER-ALL DENSITY of the earth is twice as great as the densities of its surface materials, the more gaudy theories of its interior structure—that it is hollow and peopled by another species, for instance—have had to be dropped. The earth has an inside, all right, and a pretty heavy one, but it is inaccessible to direct inspection, and not until this century have geophysical techniques become sophisticated enough to determine the broad outlines of its structure. In what follows we shall not be particularly concerned about the surface crust of the earth, to which the next chapter is devoted.

*　*　*

Probably the most valuable cohorts we have in exploring the earth's interior are earthquakes. Superficially they seem like unmitigated catastrophes, and the Lisbon earthquake that took place on All Saints' Day in 1755, killing 60,000 people, certainly could have been dispensed with, but earthquakes have their constructive aspects also.

To begin with, what *is* an earthquake? Most evidence points to sudden movements of solid rock along faults in the earth's surface as the cause of earthquakes. Such faults are the scars of earlier fractures in the crust, which occurred when the stresses developed within the earth become too great for the rock to support. An additional stress, if large enough, may cause a further slippage, and this slippage in turn sends out shock waves which may be felt over thousands of square miles in the case of a major earthquake. As far as the earth's interior is concerned, an earthquake is like a vast explosion which sends out vibrations everywhere.

Figure 6.

The vibrations set up by earthquakes are of two kinds, called *P* (for primary) and *S* (for secondary). *P* waves, as Figure 6 shows, are pressure waves, back-and-forth motions essentially the same as sound waves. *S* waves, on the other hand, are transverse motions in a rigid material in which the vibration takes place at right angles to the direction in which the wave travels. They might be compared with the vibrations in a taut string that move down the string when one end is given a quick jerk. *S* waves travel more slowly than *P* waves, and they cannot travel through liquids although *P* waves can. An easy way to distinguish between them is to think of *P* waves as *p*ush-*p*ull vibrations and *S* waves as *s*hakes.

A number of extremely sensitive instruments, called seismographs, have been devised which respond to the $P$ and $S$ waves of even distant earthquakes. Some six hundred seismological stations are in operation around the earth, and the data they obtain are routinely compared and correlated in order that the maximum information be extracted from them. It is possible to infer from seismological data the precise location of an earthquake and something about the energy released by it.

Earthquake waves do not travel in straight lines within the earth. There are two reasons for this. The first is that the velocities of the $P$ and $S$ waves vary with depth, in the case of $P$ waves from 5 miles/second to $8\frac{1}{2}$ miles/second and in the case of $S$ waves from 3 miles/second to $4\frac{1}{2}$ miles/second. Because of this variation the trajectories of earthquake waves normally are curved, as shown in Figure 7. The second source of the departure of these waves from straight lines is the presence of layers having different properties within the earth. When an earthquake wave traveling in one material passes through a boundary separating it from another material in which its speed is different, there is an abrupt deviation in the direction of the wave. Light waves offer an analogy with this behavior in the phenomenon of refraction: light has different speeds in water and air, for example, and if a person stands waist-deep in water his legs appear shortened owing to the deviation of light at the water surface.

Now let us suppose that an earthquake of satisfactory magnitude occurs somewhere. We consult the various seismological observatories, and find that most, though not all, of them have recorded $P$ waves from this event. Curiously, the stations that did not detect any $P$ waves all lie along a band from 7200 to 9700 miles distant from the earthquake (Fig. 7), and we would find, if we consulted the records of other earthquakes, that no matter where they took place similar "shadow zones" existed. This is the clue that led Oldham in

39

1906 to confirm the earlier suspicion of Wiechert that the earth's interior is made up of concentric layers.

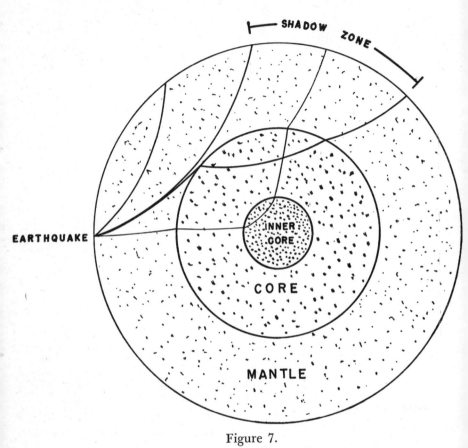

Figure 7.

Figure 7 shows why such a conclusion is necessary. In the picture the earth is divided into a central *core* and a surrounding *mantle*. *P* waves leaving the earthquake are able to go directly through the mantle only to a limited region slightly larger than a hemisphere. Those $P$ waves that impinge upon the core are bent sharply toward the center of the earth, and when they emerge they are 2500 or more miles away from those $P$ waves that just barely cleared the core. By an accurate analysis of the available data, Beno Gutenberg found, in 1914, that the mantle is 1800 miles thick, which means that the core has a radius of 2160 miles.

Supporting the above finding, and giving vital information on the nature of the core, is the behavior of the $S$ waves. These, it is found, cannot get through the core at all. The only explanation is that the core is in liquid form, which not only accounts for the absence of $S$ waves there but also for the marked changes in the velocity of $P$ waves when they enter and leave the core. The molten state of the core has other important consequences, most notably with respect to the earth's magnetism, to which we shall shortly return.

*　*　*

As time went on the division of the interior of the earth into a liquid core and a solid mantle began to be less certain. Especially sensitive seismographs detected faint traces of $P$ waves in the shadow zone, which should not have been able to get there at all. It seemed impossible to account for the appearance of such $P$ waves without attributing it, more or less vaguely, to diffraction, by analogy with the bending of light waves around the edge of an obstacle. Unfortunately this stratagem, while qualitatively fine, did not give the correct results when worked out in detail.

In 1936 Miss I. Lehmann, a Danish geophysicist, proposed that within the liquid core was a small solid inner core which could bend certain of the $P$ waves reaching it so that they could reach the shadow zone. This effect is shown schematically in Figure 7, and subsequent research has indicated that the picture suggested by Miss Lehmann is substantially correct. The precise nature of the inner core is not known, and in fact it is not clear how matter at the immense pressure of several million times atmospheric pressure can realistically be characterized as "solid" or "liquid" as we understand the terms. However, there is *something* at the center of the core that is different from the rest of the core, and $P$ waves travel faster there than in the outer part of the core.

\* \* \*

Though it is not one of the great earthquakes of history, the one that occurred on October 8, 1909, in the Croatian valley of Kulpa is noteworthy from the point of view of geophysics. From observations made on this earthquake, it became clear that there is a distinct difference between the surface regions of the earth and the underlying mantle. In fact, the line of demarcation between the mantle and the crust above it is decidedly sharp, and is known as the Mohorovičić discontinuity, after its discoverer. To the geologist, the crust and the vicissitudes it has suffered are of supreme importance, just as to a child the icing is the real point of a cake, but in fact the crust is the thinnest of layers. Under the oceans it is seldom over five miles thick, while under the continents it averages about twenty miles and may reach thirty miles under some mountain ranges.

For studying the crust explosions are superior to earthquakes, since when the are made use of the position and time of the event are usually rather well known. (The immense power of an earthquake is, however, still necessary in probing the bulk of the earth.) The usual explosions that seismologists employ are tame affairs, either normal mine and quarry blasts or special charges set off for the purpose of determining crustal structure in some locality. Sometimes, to be sure, they are in luck, and a chemical plant or munitions factory explodes in a locality infested with seismographs. Unfortunately, despite fifty years of intensive effort, the detailed nature of the crust remains obscure. There is no doubt that it is a complex affair, and no doubt that the Mohorovičić discontinuity exists, but specialists are able to agree on little else about the problem. The conclusion of the Japanese Research Group for Explosion Seismology after some recent work on crustal structure is apt: "The present results have clarified that the phenomenon which we observed and tried to interpret by means of experiment is not so simple."

\* \* \*

So far we have encountered four different layers in the earth: a central body which is probably solid, a liquid outer core surrounding it, a solid mantle, and a thin surface crust. The outer core and the mantle are apparently complex themselves, and have been divided by seismologists into two and four shells respectively. This makes a total of eight concentric layers (Figure 8) which can be distinguished apart. Of what are they composed?

Pending a hole 4000 miles deep, anything said about the earth's interior is essentially conjecture, and so conjecture is all that we have to satisfy our curiosity. Most of the evidence in hand concerning the mantle suggests that it consists of the mineral olivine, whose several forms are variations on the basic ferromagnesium silicate $(Mg, Fe)SiO_4$. But there are objections of an indirect nature to olivine: the igneous rock and lava of the crust cannot have come from olivine, and a mantle wholly of olivine would mean that the abundances of elements in the earth would differ considerably from the distribution of abundances characteristic of the universe. Accordingly, it has been suggested that the upper 200 or 300 miles of the mantle (layer *B*) consists of a basaltic rock of higher density than ordinary basalt—a suggestion

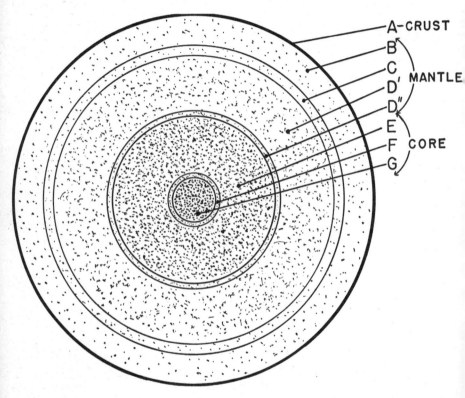

Figure 8.

that is by no means acceptable to most geophysicists. Olivine still seems the best bet. Lower in the mantle, where immense pressures are encountered (over a million pounds per square inch), the usual crystal structure of olivine has probably changed to another form, perhaps accompanied by a change in the chemical arrangement of its constituent elements. Layer *C* is a 350-mile transition layer which intervenes between the upper mantle and the fairly uniform 1200-mile thickness of the remainder of the mantle. In the latter region olivine no longer exists as such, but its components are thought to exist in separate phases such as silica, iron oxide, and magnesia. In the bottom hundred miles or so of the mantle there is an indication of the definite layer different from the main part of the mantle, but no one has any defensible idea about its composition.

Now we arrive at the liquid core, the portion of the earth which has been called upon to account for just about every aspect of the earth's behavior which has escaped attribution elsewhere. Since the material constituting the mantle is not appreciably denser than surface rocks, the core must be very heavy in order to account for the large average density of the earth. There are several clues that point to iron as the logical candidate. It has the right density, it is in the liquid state at the pressure and temperature of the core, it is a rather abundant element in the universe generally, and it is a good conductor of electricity, which is a necessary qualification in order that the earth's magnetism be explained. Because meteorites—fossil fragments left over from the creation of the solar system—contain iron only as an alloy with a little nickel, a good guess is that there is nickel in the core also.

Another idea regarding the composition of the outer core was advanced by W. H. Ramsey some years ago. He proposed that this region contains the same material as the mantle, but in a different physical state caused by high pressure such that its density has the required high value. The chief virtue of Ramsey's theory at the time it was formulated was that the

45

four small planets nearest the sun—Mercury, Venus, Earth, Mars—would thereby have the same chemical composition. Since then, however, further astronomical studies have just about ruled out this possibility, and objections on purely geophysical grounds to a nonferrous core have also turned up. Like so many other simplifying suggestions in geophysics, Ramsey's idea has had to give way before complex reality.

Between the outer and inner cores is another transition region, $F$, whose presence is known from seismic data but whose properties remain mysterious. Then we finally arrive at the inner core, the kernel of the earth. Here again all is guesswork, but the consensus is that it is mostly crystalline iron. If so, the curious situation must exist of a thick liquid layer within the earth that contains a solid center and is surrounded by a solid mantle.

How can such a structure have come into being? J. A. Jacobs has a convincing explanation. Let us plot the melting point of the earth as a function of depth, as in Figure 9. As we go farther down the temperature at which melting occurs increases owing to the greater pressures. At the boundary between the mantle and the core there is a sharp drop, corresponding to the different composition of the core, followed by another rise again caused by the mounting pressure.

Now consider the cooling down of the earth from its original wholly molten state. The variation of temperature with depth is shown by the successive thin lines, each corresponding to a different period in the earth's history. As the earth cooled, the material to solidify first is that whose melting point is reached first. According to the diagram this would have been the center of the earth, and as time went on the solid region became larger and larger. Somewhat later the innermost part of the mantle became cooled below its melting point, and the mantle thus began solidifying outward from its boundary with the core. Today the situation is presumably similar to the one represented by the lowest temperature-depth curve, with the entire mantle solid along with the central part of the core, the two separated by molten iron.

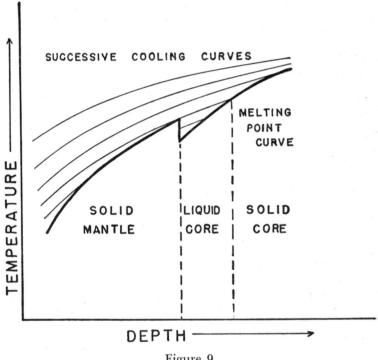

Figure 9.

As we shall learn in a moment, the earth's interior has been actually growing slightly warmer since its "formation." This is no contradiction with Figure 9, since the time of the earth's formation is usually taken to mean the time of its solidification, thereby corresponding to one of the lower of the thin-line curves shown.

* * *

Whether or not the fires of Hell lie beneath the surface of the earth, there is no doubt that it is hot enough there to satisfy most critical requirements for this region. Many lines of evidence point to the existence of such high temperatures. The most direct comes from simply taking a thermometer down into the deepest mines and wells, from which we find that, on the average, the temperature goes up by about 1° F. for every 60 feet of depth. If we were to extrapolate this rate of increase all the way down to the earth's center, the temperature there would have to be 350,000° F.—which is absurd, of course, but nevertheless an indication of the considerable temperatures that may be expected there.

Since we are able to penetrate directly into no more than the first few miles of the earth's crust, all figures that result from theoretical studies are really guesses. But the problem of the temperatures within the earth is a crucial one for hypotheses of its origin as well as for hypotheses of its structure. Part of the earth's heat comes from radioactive materials—predominantly uranium, thorium, and potassium—distributed in some manner throughout its interior, and most or all of the rest is a relic of its formation. (Some might arise from rearrangements of material in the interior.) Did the earth have a "hot" origin, condensing from a glowing gaseous nebula? Or did it have a "cold" one, accumulating its mass by collecting small particles of matter as they happened to fly past?

One clue to the temperatures inside the earth and their cause is the flow of heat outward. Measurements of this flow have been made in various locations, with the unexpected result that it is virtually the same—$1.2 \times 10^{-6}$ calories per second for each square centimeter of surface—all over the earth. The total amount of heat evolved per year is immense, being between ten and a hundred times greater than the energy involved in such geological events as volcanos and earthquakes. There is even enough heat to spare to account for mountain building and other deformations that occur in the crust. The geological history of the earth is predominantly a consequence of the steady heat streaming through its outer layers, and we owe the very existence of life to the amount and regularity of this flow.

It is worth noting, by the way, that the uniformity of heat emanation over the continents and oceans presents a paradoxical problem of its own. Underneath the continental land masses the earth's crust is about twenty miles deep and consists largely of granite. Now granite is rich in uranium, thorium, and potassium, and the radioactivity of these elements in a fifteen-mile-thick layer of granite is sufficient to account for the entire observed heat flow. Added to the thermal efflux from the interior, the heat that should be generated in the granite substructure of the continents yields, if anything, too high a figure for agreement with the observed value. On the other hand, only three to six miles of crust support the oceans, and most of the oceanic rock is basalt which has a third the radioactive content of granite. Thus the heat flow through the ocean floor should be smaller than the observed value, certainly much less than the continental heat flow. Yet both are essentially identical.

The most obvious explanation, that the mantle under the oceans is hotter than it is under the continents, seems to be ruled out, since the 500-1000° F. temperature difference required is too large not to be detected. The least objectionable of the other arguments holds that the radioactivity initially in the outer mantle somehow migrated to the crust under the land masses, while it still remains part of the mantle under the oceans. To make up for the greater depth of the oceanic heat sources, a very efficient means of heat transmission must exist in the mantle. It has been suggested that convection—the physical flow of heated fluids, for instance, the rising of hot air above a radiator—takes place there, although it is perhaps hard to imagine a mantle sufficiently rigid to support the vibrations of seismic $S$ waves also being able to exhibit convection currents. A sticky problem.

\* \* \*

Let us return to the more fundamental subject of heat in the earth as a whole. One way of determining its present interior temperature is to trace the thermal history of our planet from its birth 4½ billion years ago, combining the effects of the cooling down from its initial temperature and the heating up from radioactivity. We must first guess at the initial temperature, and fortunately most of the guesses that have been made fall into only two categories. The members of the hot origin school have given estimates in the range 9000-14,000° F. for the center, dropping to the neighborhood of 1000° F. at the surface. Those in favor of a cold origin, however, think that a temperature of roughly 1000° F. prevailed throughout the entire primeval earth.

The four isotopes involved in the radioactive heating are potassium 40, uranium 235, uranium 238, and thorium 232. (Ordinary potassium contains only a minute fraction of its radioactive isotope, but there is enough potassium in the earth for it to be significant.) We now must estimate the amounts of these isotopes that are present and their distribution. By combining these guesses with the conjectured original temperatures, we can find, with the help of a large computing machine, what has been happening to the earth since its formation. The results show that in the interior, below about 500 miles from the surface, the earth has been growing warmer and warmer from the beginning. At the core-mantle boundary, the temperature has gone up about 500° F. The top layers heated up at first, but after an initial billion years or so began a gradual cooling.

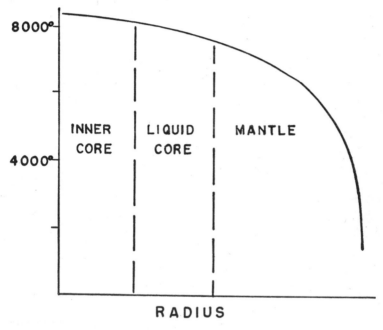

Figure 10.

A strong point in favor of this hypothetical thermal history of the earth is that it suggests that the crust may have been so strongly heated in the billion years after the earth was formed that it remelted. This would account for the puzzling fact that, although the earth is about 4½ billions

51

years old, rocks older than 3 billion years have never been found.

The present temperature distribution throughout the earth is believed to follow a curve like the one shown in Figure 10. There is a large difference in temperature between the top of the mantle, which is below 2000° F., and the inner region, where temperatures of over 7000° F. prevail. At the core boundary, the temperature is about 7800° F., and from there it rises only slowly to 8600° F. at the very center. This is not much cooler than the 11,000° F. temperature of the surface of the sun—but it is a lot cooler than the 35,000,-000° F. estimated for the sun's center.

# FOUR

# The Crust

THE CRUST OF THE EARTH, AN EPIDERMIS OF MINUTE THICK-
ness, is the most accessible part of our planet to measurement
and study, and accordingly we know a great deal about it.
Its gross features have been mapped, its mountains scaled, its
ocean depths plumbed. But the crust is far from being a permanent structure, and its present configuration is only a
phase in a violent history. The role of the geophysicist here is
that of biographer, to reconstruct the evolution of the crust
from ill-preserved relics with the help of what he would call
"educated guesses"—which lie halfway between the products
of women's intuition and of poetic license. The crust has a
poor memory, and delights in obscuring its past by smooth-
ing down the rough places and filling in the hollows; but it
cannot suppress the rumblings indicative of inner turmoil,
and so we have a better than sporting chance of arriving at
the truth.

\* \* \*

Let us begin with the continents and oceans. There is a
curious kind of balance between them, with major land areas

53

tending to lie directly opposite major water areas. Three-quarters of the earth's land is contained in Europe, Africa, and Asia, whose center is on the other side of the earth from the center of the Pacific Ocean, whose 70 million square miles make it the greatest ocean. The Antarctic continent (which is not quite centered about the South Pole) has its antipode in the North Atlantic Ocean. In fact, the earth as a whole may be divided into two hemispheres (Figure 11), one

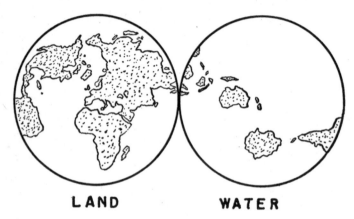

**LAND**            **WATER**

Figure 11.

made up of 46 per cent land and the other with less than 10 per cent. The land hemisphere would have its pole in the English Channel, while the pole of the water hemisphere would be located southeast of New Zealand.

The pattern of the continents has another striking feature —if North and South America were to be slid across the Atlantic, they would mesh like pieces of a jigsaw puzzle with the western edges of Europe and Africa. Left behind would be a vast gash, larger than the present Pacific Ocean. The moon exhibits an equally remarkable feature—it presents the same face to the earth at all times. Dare we conjecture from these facts that the moon was once part of the earth, only to have some cataclysm split it off from what is today the Pacific?

After a few calculations the idea looks even better. If the moon and the earth were once a single object with the same total angular momentum they divide between themselves at present, the combination would have rotated once every four hours instead of once every twenty-four. To see how this comes about, think of an ice skater starting a spin with one leg and both arms outstretched. When he brings them in close to his body, he spins much faster than before. The same effect would have the earth spinning faster if the moon were part of it.

We next compute the period of oscillation of the earth-moon. Every object has a certain natural vibrational frequency: pluck the A string on a violin, and it will vibrate 440 times per second each time this is done. If the earth-moon were "plucked" somehow, it would quiver once every two hours. Further, if this plucking took place in time with the natural oscillations—a condition known as resonance—the size of the oscillations would grow larger and larger. This is the principle behind the fabled disintegration of goblets when exposed to sound waves of precisely the same frequency as their own natural frequency. And the four-hour rotation of the earth-moon provides, via the twice-daily tides that would have been raised by the sun (see Chapter 5), a regular disturbance whose period of two hours is the same as the natural period of oscillation of the earth-moon itself. What could be more natural than to have immense vibrations take place, culminating in the breaking off of a great blob which later condensed into the moon?

Alas, while elegant in the extreme, this notion of the origin of the moon and continents will not do. A careful analysis of all the factors involved shows that, even if an

55

earth-moon ever existed in one piece (which is unlikely), tidal oscillations could not have disrupted it to the extent needed for a fragment the size of the moon to split away. And, as a clincher, it has been pointed out that a fragment cast off by the earth in this way would inevitably have been drawn back in a short time.

* * *

Before going further into the various ideas regarding the origin of the continents and oceans, a closer look into some of the characteristics of these surface features will be helpful. The earth's crust may very roughly be divided into two levels, a continental one about 3000 feet above sea level and an oceanic one about 13,000 feet below sea level. Why do the continents not sink down until the entire crust is at the same level? Their weight is surely immense, and in the eons since they came into being even the stiffest underlying material would have yielded enough to make possible such a leveling out.

We have already mentioned a clue to the solution of this mystery, although without emphasizing its significance. The crust, as measured from the Mohorovičić discontinuity, is much thicker beneath the continents than beneath the oceans. At first glance this seems only to magnify the difficulty of explaining the support of the continental masses, but when we recall that the earth as a whole is double the density of the crust, everything fits together.

Suppose that we place several blocks of wood, of different sizes, in a pool of water. The larger ones float higher than the smaller, while simultaneously extending down farther into the water (Figure 12). Thus if the crust is imagined as floating in equilibrium on a denser mantle capable of plastic deformation, we have the analogue of wooden blocks of different sizes floating in water. This implies, if carried to its logical end, that exceptionally elevated regions—mountain ranges and plateaus—have corresponding roots extending an exceptional distance downward. Such is actually the case, and in fact its discovery led Airy a century ago to propose the floating of the entire crust. The idea that irregularities in the crust are supported because of their buoyancy is known as *isostasy*.

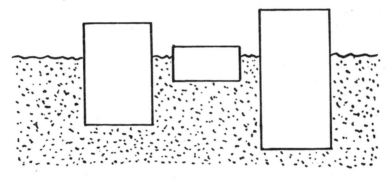

Figure 12.

Isostasy had its beginning in the classic survey of India carried out by Sir George Everest. Plumb lines were used to determine the latitudes of Kaliana, adjacent to the Himalayan plateau, and of Kalianpur, several hundred miles to the south. When these figures were compared with the surveyed distance between the two places, there was a disagreement beyond the limits of error. The answer seemed to be that the Himalayas were deflecting the plumb bob at Kaliana away from the center of the earth, but taking the supposedly extra mass of the mountains into account produced a correction factor three times greater than the one needed. Airy's interpretation was that the relatively light rock which constitutes the Himalayas is present to a considerable depth be-

57

neath it as well, accounting for the only slight deviation of the Kaliana plumb bob.

The view that crustal projections, such as mountains and the continents themselves, are all perfectly balanced isostatically with the help of roots of light material is a useful and valuable one, but it is not true everywhere. In island arcs such as the East and West Indies, for instance, isostasy fails to explain gravity data. But, we may legitimately argue, there is no reason why the entire crust should be in complete equilibrium; there is plenty of evidence for continual fracturing and folding activity, symptomatic of crustal instability.

Before leaving isostasy we must account for the apparent discrepancy between our regarding of the mantle as solid from the point of view of seismology and as liquid from the point of view of having the crust floating on it. The discrepancy becomes less significant, though, when we recall that the S waves caused by earthquakes, which require a solid for their propagation, represent rather fast vibrations, while the isostatic rising and sinking of crustal masses can take place over long periods of time. Even the most brittle solids we know give way under sufficient pressure, and this is particularly true of such noncrystalline substances as glass. Glass is so rigid that it will shatter rather than yield to a blow, but if enough time is provided it will deform under even the slight pressure of its own weight. This seems to be the case with the mantle. Ten thousand years ago Scandinavia was covered with thick ice sheet; with the melting of the ice the peninsula grew lighter and therefore more buoyant, and has been rising ever since at a geologically rapid rate. This "rapid rate" is about a foot per century—so the mantle is solid enough.

\* \* \*

If the crust of today floats upon the mantle, may it not simply represent a kind of scum which rose to the surface while the mantle was still molten? In many ways this is an attractive hypothesis. In particular, the segregation of the light granite rock into discrete continents would be a natural consequence of the convection currents—like the circulatory currents in a pan of boiling water—that must have been present.

While the primitive earth was still fluid, convection was unimpeded, and the early continents probably had a fairly simple pattern. A calculation by Pekeris, for instance, shows that this process should have resulted in a pair of continents, each centered about a pole, with a belt of ocean in between. Subsequently a separate, very dense iron core came into being, and radioactive materials were transported upward near the surface. The appearance of the core together with the change in the temperature distribution in the earth's interior added to the complexity of the current systems in the mantle, leading to the wrecking of the infant continents. The fragments of the latter then more or less wandered around until they came to rest in their present configuration when the upper mantle solidified. The ocean floors and the substratum holding the granite continents in place, then, are representative of the mantle. Jeffreys finds that if continental evolution occurred in a manner like the above one, the general distribution of land and water masses that we find follows naturally.

A quite different theory also has its supporters. J. T. Wilson, a principal exponent, has the young earth encased in a skin of heavy basaltic rock. Here and there bits of lighter granite forced their way through, forming nuclei which proceeded to collect other light materials around them. When the nuclei grew beyond a certain point fractures would occur around their margins, permitting additional molten rock to come forth and add to their bulk. There is no reason why this process of continental growth should not be in progress today, and there are indications, in the form of regularities in the locations of seismic and volcanic activity, that this may be the case.

\* \* \*

While we cannot say for sure whether the continents rose boldly through the mantle or made their way to prominence by a more gradual process, there is much that we can say about their subsequent history. The big question here is the matter of continental drift, a brilliant, closely reasoned, and once widely-believed idea whose factual basis, like the Cheshire cat, has imperceptibly vanished into thin air.

The theory of continental drift was originally devised by Alfred Wegener as a means of explaining the parallel evolution of living things throughout the world. Going back through the ages, the fossil record shows that whenever a new species appeared it did so everywhere that a suitable habitat existed. There are, of course, a few isolated exceptions—kangaroos are purely Australian—but, for the most part, evolution proceeded at the same rate on all the continents and in all the oceans.

The standard explanation for this uniform biological development was a series of land bridges linking the continents together plus a series of channels joining the oceans. After a while, as paleontology developed, more and more bridges and channels became necessary. It does not take much imagination to predict what happened: half the biologists had bridges between the various continental regions, while the other half claimed that channels separated them in the same places. And, furthermore, what became of the various bridges and channels? It is hard to see how, with their deep roots, the bridges could have descended into the sea to vanish completely. Wegener was on firm ground when he searched for an alternative to this scheme.

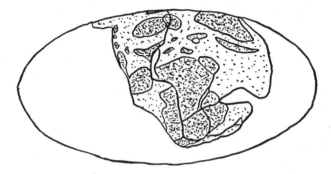

Figure 13.

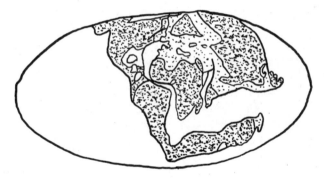

Figure 14.

What Wegener suggested instead was that, a few hundred million years ago, the continents had a radically different arrangement than they have now. His idea was that the globe looked something like Figure 13 then, with North America

61

and Europe joined together while South America, Africa, India, and Australia composed the continent of Gondwanaland. Later, as time went on, the pattern changed to Figure 14, and ultimately to what we have at present. Wegener took quite seriously the "floating" of the continents on a plastic substratum, and held that if up-and-down movements are possible, horizontal ones are also.

This drifting of the continents over the face of the earth found support in data regarding prehistoric climates. A little over two hundred thousand years ago South Africa, India, Australia, and part of South America were burdened with great ice sheets, while at the same time a tropical rain forest covered North America, Europe, and China. At various other times, there was sufficient vegetation in Alaska and Antarctica for coal desposits to have resulted, and so currently frigid a place as Baffin Bay was a desert. Wegener and his associates examined what was known about the climates of the distant past and tried to arrange the continents at each geological period so that the glaciers were near the poles and the hot moist regions were near the equator. Since the continents were allegedly free to move about, this seemed easy enough to do.

Continental drift, then, has some very attractive aspects. It is when we examine the forces that were supposed to have pushed the continents from place to place that we meet with difficulty. The principal force invoked by Wegener was the one discovered by Baron Roland von Eötvös in 1910. Eötvös found that a mass floating on the surface of a rotating liquid sphere of nonuniform composition will tend to move toward its equator. As a consequence of the resulting equatorward motion, Wegener supposed that a westerly drift would also occur. A meteorologist by profession, he was familiar with the fact that the effect of the earth's rotation on moving air masses—which appear as winds—is to cause in them a deflection to the right in the Northern Hemisphere and a deflection to the left in the Southern. If the floating land masses behave in this way also, their progress to the equator under the influence of the Eötvös force would result in a westerly drift.

The trouble is that the Eötvös force is a relatively minute one. If the continents were floating in a real liquid, even small forces would suffice to produce perceptible motion. However, the mantle, while deformable in the sense that modeling clay is, is hardly liquid; a careful analysis by Sir Harold Jeffreys shows that the most rapid possible drift would only amount to a mile every hundred thousand years. In addition, Wegener considered the crustal layer beneath the ocean floor as so weak that it would not impede the drifting continents. Unfortunately this layer happens to be exceedingly strong and rigid, more so than the continental blocks themselves—so that if enough force was present, the continents would buckle first. (The latter, in fact, is believed to be one of the causes of mountain building. According to Jeffreys, "it is hard to see how any mountains at all could be formed without something strong pushing the continents from all sides.")

*   *   *

With continental drift out of the question, what shall we do about the near-simultaneity of evolution around the world and the radical changes in climate in the past half-billion years? Without pretending to be the final word, two types of geophysical processes have been suggested which offer at least partial answers and have the paramount virtue of obeying the laws of nature. The first concerns probable changes that have occurred in the topography of the earth, which would affect climate as well as promote the migration

63

of animal and plant life from continent to continent. Let us look at a specific example.

From the Arctic to the Antarctic a great range of mountains runs under the Atlantic Ocean, neatly following a middle course between the Americas on one side and Europe and Africa on the other. Here and there—the Azores, Ascension Island, Tristan da Cunha—this Mid-Atlantic Ridge pokes through the water, but for the most part its presence can be detected only by deep-sea sounding instruments. Despite this there are places in the Ridge where samples of the sediment forming the ocean bottom are littered with fossil *fresh-water* diatom shells. The fifteen thousand or so varieties of these microscopic algae are divided into salt- and fresh-water types, which can be distinguished by the markings on their durable silica shells. Fresh-water diatom shells on the floor of the ocean can mean only one thing: at one time this region must have been above sea level, and the diatoms lived in ponds or lakes at those spots.

There is, then, good reason to believe that the entire Mid-Atlantic Ridge once projected from the ocean, forming an immense north-south land barrier and providing the basis for an ambitious theory. According to the latter the Ridge blocked the Gulf Stream, keeping its warm waters from the now land-locked Arctic. Meanwhile a southern current originating on the other side of the Ridge provided a source of balmy moist air to North Africa and the Iberian peninsula, making them huge verdant gardens and enabling them to support an extensive civilization. All this time, of course, the vast, barren glaciation of the most recent ice age covered northern Europe and America.

Then, about ten thousand years ago, the Mid-Atlantic Ridge began to sink. The Gulf Stream flowed north uninterrupted, melting the glaciers and bringing a milder climate. But along with the northeast arc of the warm Gulf

Spiral nebula in Ursa Major. The Milky Way, in which the sun occupies
a position near the rim, is believed to be shaped somewhat like this.
(*Yerkes Observatory*)

The moon, showing its "seas," which are actually deposits of nonreflecting matter, and its "craters," whose origin is unknown but may have been due to meteor impacts or volcanic activity. (*Yerkes Observatory*)

The earth as seen from a U.S. Navy Viking rocket fired in New Mexico in 1954. The picture is a composite of several photographs and shows 600,000 square miles of the earth's surface, mainly in Texas and Mexico. The rocket reached an altitude of 158 miles. (*U.S. Navy*)

Plastic balloons containing helium are frequently used for sounding the upper atmosphere in search of data on cosmic rays, the aurora, ozone, and meteorological variables such as temperature, pressure, humidity, and winds. (*U.S. Air Force*)

Cosmic ray monitor near Fairbanks, Alaska, keeps continuous record of sea level neutron intensity. Technician is adjusting barograph. Above his head is a panel on which are mounted a barometer, thermometer, voltage and frequency meters to detect any changes in electrical power supply, and registers indicating number of neutrons detected. The motion picture camera at right photographs the panel at frequent intervals. (*New York University*)

A portable gravimeter being used in the field to determine the local intensity of the earth's gravitational field. This information is valuable in prospecting for oil and minerals as well as in assessing the true shape of the earth. (*Texas Instruments, Inc., Harper Leiper Studios*)

*Top:* Dr. Maurice Ewing inspecting recording drums of monitor seismographs at Columbia University's Lamont Geological Observatory which he directs. Laboratory is near New York City. (*Lamont Geological Observatory*) *Bottom:* Seismographs at Southern Methodist University. Instrument in foreground measures horizontal vibrations of earthquakes, the one in background vertical vibrations. Both were designed by Dr. Hugo Benioff. (*The Geotechnical Corporation*)

Scientists aboard the schooner *Vema* preparing to stream "fish" containing precision magnetometer for measuring intensity of earth's magnetic field. (*Lamont Geological Observatory*)

Stream flows the southwest arc of the cold Canary Current, carrying chill northern water down to the tropics where it is heated before replenishing the Gulf Stream on the other side of the Atlantic. The consequent change in North African climate converted the once green Sahara into an immense desert, in this picture, driving its inhabitants eastward toward Egypt in a migration that is part of history. We can speculate that the Atlantis of Plato had its genesis in legends told Rameses III and his court by visitors (or captives) whose ancestors knew of the former glory of the Mid-Atlantic Ridge.

* * *

Geological events of this kind, which also provide stepping stones across the oceans, offer part of the solution to the evolution problem. When combined with the possibility of the migration of spores, seeds, perhaps even eggs, on debris carried along by ocean currents, we have a case which, though marginal, does less violence to the facts than continental drift. We do not want a theory which makes biological mixing *too* rapid a process, and some such explanation as the above may well end up being accepted.

With regard to the climatic problem, local changes in the crust, helpful in certain specific situations, are not entirely sufficient. What will do the trick is a sliding of the entire crust over the mantle, leading to an apparent wandering of the poles. This sounds at first more wild than continental drift, but it actually has a much more secure foundation. Given polar wandering, frigid, temperate, and torrid climates would move across the world, and such anomalies as coal in Antarctica and glaciers in India need puzzle us no longer.

The arguments we have given against continental drift, namely the weakness of the only forces that might cause it and the stiffness of the ocean floor, do not apply to polar wandering. With a time scale of some hundreds of millions of years, the adhesion between crust and mantle—which is to say, the plasticity of the upper mantle—is not too great for perfectly reasonable forces to produce the sliding indicated by paleoclimatology.

F. A. Vening Meinesz has worked out the effect on the crust of convection currents in the mantle similar to the ones presumed to have participated in forming the continents. If the crust has shifted by 90° relative to the earth's axis in a half-billion years, the internal currents must have been flowing at the rate of a few inches per year. This figure is acceptable on the basis of what we know about the mantle, but we must bear in mind the distinction between the possible and the actual.

More recently Thomas Gold has examined polar wandering from a different point of view. A beetle on the earth's crust will cause it to move relative to the axis of rotation merely by sitting in the right place for long enough. In the same way, a newly-formed projection from the earth's crust —say a young mountain range which has not had time to subside into the mantle or be substantially eroded—can lead to polar wandering. For example, if a continental mass the size of South America were suddenly to rise by forty feet, the crust would slide over the mantle at the rate of several hundred feet per year until the projection reached the equator. Gold's suggestion is a promising one, particularly since the crust is known periodically to undergo convulsions which furrow its surface.

We shall return to polar wandering in Chapter 6, where some very strong evidence in favor of it will be described.

# FIVE

# Time and Tide

THESE ARE UNSETTLED TIMES, AND DESPITE THE FADING OF Nature's grand gaucheries before the grander gaucheries of man, one hesitates to bring up a topic so intrinsically troubling as the running down of the earth's rotation. Still, the effect is there, and in attempting to account for it we shall find ourselves successively in the tidal cataracts of the sea, the diffuse gas of interplanetary space, and the turbulent molten iron of the earth's core.

The changing length of the day is no novel idea, having been discovered by Halley in 1695. What Halley found, to be exact, was that the moon seemed to be going faster and faster around the earth. His figures, obtained by comparing the current lunar observations with ancient eclipse records, were confirmed in subsequent work. A half century later the philosopher Immanuel Kant, in a work entitled *Utersuchung der Frage, ob die Erde in ihrer Umdrehung un die Achse, wodurch sie die Abwechselung des Tages und der Nacht hervorbringt, eine Veränderung seit den ersten Zeiten ihres Ursprunges erlitten habe, und woraus man sich ihrer versichern Könne,* suggested that what was really happening was

67

that the earth was spinning more slowly on its axis, and that the moon only appeared to be going faster. His acute guess was that tidal friction—which we shall speak of in some detail —was responsible for the slowing down.

Some years later Laplace, the French mathematician and astronomer, rejected Kant's hypothesis on the grounds that if the rate of rotation of the earth were really diminishing, the sun and the other planets as well as the moon would seem to be accelerating. Such accelerations were not found, and Laplace put forward the idea that, owing to the continuing distortion of the earth's orbit caused by the gravitational attractions of the other planets, the sun's pull on the moon is decreasing and the moon speeding up in consequence. Laplace's theory seemed to agree with the data, but subsequently he was found to have overlooked an intricate point which, when corrected for, threw his figures far below the actual ones.

Finally, in 1905, it was established that the sun indeed is accelerating relative to the earth, and later research showed that the same is true for Mercury and Venus. The accelerations of the sun, moon, and Mercury and Venus (corresponding accelerations of the other planets are too small to be detected) can all be accounted for if the earth is slowing down so as to make the day longer by about one second every 100,000 years. While this is hardly an alarming rate, and even if it were there is nothing that could be done about it, it is interesting to investigate its cause or causes.

Let us first detour for a moment to inquire into the tides, which, just as Kant suggested, are intimately connected with the earth's rotation.

\* \* \*

When we think of the seas and oceans of the globe, we tend to envision them as vast sheets of water, normally quiescent but on occasion stirred to spasms of destructive violence by storms. Yet beneath the irregularly changing surface of the sea there is a steady, regular pulsation—the tides.

The advanced civilizations surrounding the Mediterranean in ancient times were, by and large, oblivious to tides and tidal currents, whose manifestations in this almost landlocked sea are negligible. However, the more daring mariners of these civilizations, who ventured through the Pillars of Hercules into the great ocean beyond, and the peoples dwelling on the shores of what are now Spain, France, England, and Scandinavia all knew something of the rhythm of the tides. They knew that at new moon and full moon the difference between high water and low water is much larger than it is when only half of the moon's disc is visible, and that at the equinoxes (when the sun is overhead at the equator marking the starts of spring and fall) the tides are higher than at the solstices (when the sun is farthest north or farthest south, marking the starts of summer and winter). The fog of medieval superstition managed to obscure much of this knowledge. Thus King John, the year after having had the Magna Carta wrested from him, lost much of his army and supplies in the flood tide at the Wash, a bay in eastern England. (He died a week after this unexpected, though predictable, catastrophe, largely from the aftereffects of vexation.)

Kepler, who discovered the laws of planetary motion, also suspected a direct connection between the moon and the tides. This was scoffed at by Galileo, who ridiculed Kepler for having "given his ear and assent to the moon's predominancy over the water, and to occult properties and such like trifles." To be fair, Kepler *was* an astrologer, and many of his notions were absurd, but Galileo would have been better advised to look into the matter before denouncing Kepler's idea.

69

Not until Newton was the cause of the tides finally ascribed to the gravitational effects of the moon and, to a smaller extent, the sun. At first glance the mechanism seems obvious: the moon pulls the waters of the earth toward it, and as the earth rotates the positions of high and low tide stay the same with respect to the moon but shift with respect to the earth. This picture is totally incorrect. For one thing, almost everywhere there are two, not one, tidal cycles per day of about 12½ hours each. For another, the sun's gravitational force on the earth greatly exceeds that of the moon—but the tides follow the moon. A more subtle analysis is required.

The key to the origin of the tides is that the effective force exerted by a heavenly body on the waters of the world is the *difference* between the average force exerted by that body on the earth as a whole and the force it exerts on the oceans. Because the sun is very far away, there is not much difference between these forces. The moon, on the other hand, is sufficiently close to the earth so that its pull on the waters nearest it is greater than its pull on the rest of the earth. Hence the

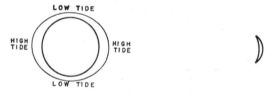

Figure 15.

tidal bulge toward the moon in Figure 15. Its pull on the waters on the opposite side of the earth is correspondingly less than its average pull on the earth, and so these waters bulge out away from the moon as in the same drawing. The two bulges correspond to high tide, while the two intermediate flattened water surfaces correspond to low tide.

Let us consider this problem more quantitatively. The moon is a mean distance of 239,000 miles away from the earth's center, and it is closer by the earth's radius of 4000 miles to a body of water which has the moon overhead. Since the force of gravity varies with the square of the distance, the effective pull on the water is about 1/30th greater than the average pull on the earth. Similarly, the effective pull on a body of water on the other side of the earth is about 1/30th less than the average pull on the earth.

What is the average force that the moon exerts on the earth? When the answer is worked out, it turns out that this force on any object amounts to roughly 0.00033 per cent of the weight of the object. To put it another way, the attraction of the moon for something weighing 15 tons is only a pound. But the differential force on this object—that is, the tide-producing force—is 1/30th as much, or about half an ounce.

It does not take much perception to see that so trifling a force is not capable of bodily lifting the oceans by several feet. However, while the moon cannot raise the tides directly, it is able to achieve this result by sliding the waters of the seas and oceans horizontally. Anyone can manage to budge a boat weighing several tons in still water, even though lifting it is out of the question. It is because water flows so readily that tides occur. In Figure 16 is a diagram showing the moon's effective force around the earth; each arrow points in the direction of the force in its vicinity, and its length indicates the strength of the force. Figure 17 shows the horizontal components of these forces, that is, their projections along the earth's surface. It is the forces of Figure 17 that influence the tides.

71

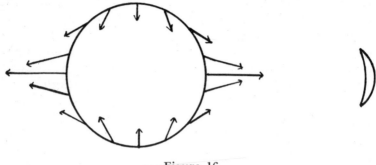

Figure 16.

The sun is less than half as effective as the moon in producing tides. Its influence is largely confined to increasing the range of the tides when it is in line with the moon and earth at full and new moon to cause spring tides, and to decreasing

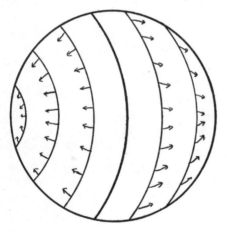

Figure 17.

the range of the tides when it acts at right angles to the moon at first quarter and last quarter.

As the earth rotates, the tidal bulges are restrained by the moon's attraction from moving with it. If the earth were perfectly smooth, the bulges would point directly toward and away from the moon while the earth rotated underneath. However, the earth has a rather ragged profile, and by a kind of frictional force its waters are dragged along with it as it turns. The tidal bulges therefore point slightly to the east of

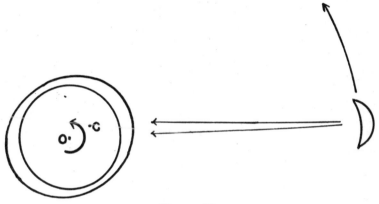

Figure 18.

a line joining the centers of the earth and moon as in Figure 18. The earth must continually expend energy to keep moving about its axis despite the retarding effects of the tides. Or, to look at the same situation from a different angle, the energy used up by tidal currents must be replenished at the expense of the earth's rotation. Either way the conclusion is that the earth must be slowing down very gradually, and the length of the day increasing at a corresponding rate.

The tidal bulge nearest the moon is always a little ahead of where it would be if there were no tidal friction. In the course of revolving around the earth, then, the moon is actually being attracted by a gravitational force that is not quite centered in the middle of the earth $O$, but rather is a bit forward of this point at the location $C$. Therefore the earth, by virtue of the displaced tidal bulges, acts to pull the moon forward in its path. The speeding up of the moon can be distinguished from the slowing down of the earth by comparison with the sun, Mercury, and Venus, and it is a measurable effect.

\* \* \*

The first successful calculation of tidal friction was made in 1919 by G. I. Taylor, grandson of the logician Boole, Nehru's rowing coach, noted anchor designer, and brilliant and versatile physicist. In the oceans of the world the tidal velocities are only a few feet per hour. However, in a number of small, relatively shallow, and partially enclosed seas considerable tidal currents occur whose strengths are measured in miles per hour rather than feet per hour. Taylor made a detailed calculation of the energy loss in the Irish Sea, the apparently insignificant body of water separating Ireland from England. He found it to be $3 \times 10^{17}$ ergs/sec., thirty times more than the energy dissipation in all open oceans.

No one expected, of course, that the Irish Sea all by itself was slowing down the earth's rotation. The important thing about Taylor's value was that he came up with it twice, using a different procedure each time—a strong indication that he was on the right track. Harold Jeffreys then extended Taylor's analysis to most of the shallow seas, bays, and channels of the world. He found that two-thirds of all of the energy loss resulting from tidal friction takes place in the Bering Sea, with nearly all of the rest occurring in the Irish Sea, the North Sea, and the English Channel in Europe, the Yellow

Sea, Sea of Okhotsk, and Malacca Strait in Asia, and Fox Strait and the Bay of Fundy in North America. The grand total was a little over $10^{19}$ ergs/sec., which is an average figure since tidal velocities vary each lunar month from maxima at the spring tides to minima at the neap tides.

Jeffreys was able to account for 80 per cent of the then-accepted rate of slowing down of the earth, which, considering the fairly crude marine data he had to work with, seemed to take care of the problem. In recent years better clocks have been devised which indicate that the slowing down is more rapid than had been thought, but no similar revision has been found justified in the tidal figures. We must look elsewhere to another source of dissipation.

*   *   *

At this point we leave the comfortable sanctuary of accepted doctrines and enter the wilder realm of the speculative. Very recently the author proposed a theory to account for the increasing length of the day which, while still tentative, is apparently not in disagreement with any existing knowledge. This theory had its roots in an attempt to account for a puzzling problem in cosmic rays. These "rays" are actually high-energy atomic nuclei which are accelerated in the depths of our galaxy and continually impinge on the earth. The ones striking the top of the atmosphere are called primary cosmic rays. They interact with the nuclei of the oxygen and nitrogen in the atmosphere to produce secondary cosmic rays, which are what reach the earth's surface. The secondaries include neutrons, protons, and alpha particles, which are essentially the debris of disintegrated nuclei; mesons of various kinds, which are very short-lived particles produced in high-energy nuclear collisions; and showers of electrons and gamma rays which originate in the decay of

75

certain kinds of mesons and multiply in numbers as they proceed downward.

Primary cosmic rays all carry positive electrical charges, and as they approach the earth from the far reaches of galactic space they are affected by the magnetic field of the earth. Relatively low energy primaries (below 14 billion electron volts) are deflected by this field so that they tend to follow the magnetic lines of force toward the higher latitudes (Fig-

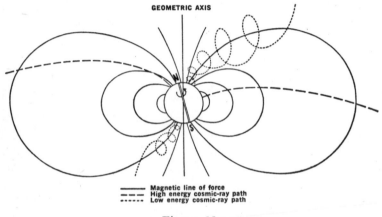

GEOMETRIC AXIS

——— Magnetic line of force
— — — High energy cosmic-ray path
······ Low energy cosmic-ray path

Figure 19.

ure 19). High-energy primaries are able to get through the magnetic field anywhere. Because many primaries are of low energy, the cosmic-ray intensity at the earth varies with location, being a minimum at the equator and increasing toward the poles. Thus cosmic rays act as probes to enable us to determine the characteristics of the geomagnetic field causing their geographic variation.

Several years ago an extensive survey of cosmic-ray neutron intensity was carried out. Special neutron counters were installed on two ships, one of which circumnavigated the entire North American continent while the other proceeded down to Antarctica via New Zealand. The result was a comprehensive picture of cosmic-ray neutron intensity around the world. From this picture the effective external magnetic field of the earth was reconstructed—and it turned out to be quite different from the field computed on the basis of magnetic data obtained at the earth's surface.

In attempting to explain the discrepancy between the two fields it is necessary to assume that interplanetary space is a conductor of electricity. The traditional view is that the solar system is almost devoid of matter except for such objects as planets, satellites, comets, and meteors. However, current astrophysical thought favors an interplanetary region filled with a tenuous gas consisting mainly of ionized hydrogen. If this is correct, and it seems probable that it is, then the motion of the lines of force of the geomagnetic field as they rotate with the earth must induce electric currents in the surrounding interplanetary matter. The theory underlying this process is the same as that governing the operation of a dynamo, where current is generated in wires moving through a magnetic field.

The system of currents that is induced in interplanetary space in this way extends several earth's radii outward. The currents have a magnetic field of their own, just as the current in the coils of an electromagnet has associated with it a magnetic field. When the details are worked out, the magnetic field of the induced currents is of precisely the right kind to produce the observed discrepancy between the magnetic field originating in the earth's interior and the field that influences the motion of primary cosmic rays.

Energy must be fed into any electric current if it is to continue without gradually dying out. Here the energy is supplied by the earth's rotation, which must push the lines

77

of force of its magnetic field through interplanetary space. We can legitimately think of the conducting interplanetary gas as exerting a kind of electromagnetic viscous drag on the lines of force, something like that exerted by water on a moving boat. When the amount of this drag is computed, it turns out that the power needed to maintain the earth's rotation against the electromagnetic drag is approximately $2 \times 10^{19}$ erg/sec.—twice the rate of energy loss by tidal friction. While this figure may have to be revised somewhat upward or downward as more data become available, there is much in favor of the idea that the gradual slowing down of the spinning earth originates in part in electromagnetic phenomena taking place many thousands of miles out in the virtual void of interplanetary space.

\* \* \*

Further to complicate matters, two plausible mechanisms have been proposed that would act to *increase* the speed of the earth's rotation.

One of them was put forward a few years ago by Harold Urey to account for the disturbing fact that the moon was apparently increasing in velocity, because of tidal attraction, faster than it should have in relation to the observed slowing down of the earth. The status of this discrepancy is today not entirely clear, in addition to the existence of an alternate theory, and so Urey's proposal has been met with careful scrutiny by geophysicists, who do not agree on how large an acceleration it can cause. In brief, Urey suggested that the moment of inertia (which determines how fast a body will rotate when given a twist) of the earth is decreasing as iron in the mantle sinks into the core. This would have an effect identical with that obtained by a spinning skater who draws his outstretched arms close to his body, which results in his spinning faster. Granted that iron may be migrating down-ward into the core, the problem—still outstanding—is to find a credible way for this to occur rapidly enough to influence perceptibly the rotation of the earth.

The other idea, equally farfetched to some, is one with such elegant implications that it would be a pity if it were not correct. This is based on a curious coincidence first noted by Lord Kelvin in 1882: the earth's atmosphere has a period of oscillation exactly half—as far as we can tell—of the length of the day.

To describe again what is meant by period of oscillation, strike a portion of gelatin with a spoon. The gelatin quivers. No matter where or how hard the gelatin is struck, the number of its vibrations per second is always the same. The time needed for a single vibration is called the period of oscillation.

By striking the gelatin exactly in time with its normal quivers, the size of the vibrations grows larger and larger. Now the sun's radiation heats up the atmosphere, causing it to expand, and this occurs regularly once each day. Since the atmosphere has a twelve-hour natural period of oscilla-tion, this is equivalent to striking it every other time it vibrates. The result should be unusually large pressure fluc-tuations twice a day, which indeed are found. In other words, the atmosphere experiences tides exactly like the sea, except that they follow the sun rather than the moon and have a quite different cause.

Kelvin went on from here to point out that, because the atmospheric tides have their maxima behind a line from the earth to the sun, the solar gravitational attraction tends to pull the nearest bulge farther in the direction of the earth's rotation. Thus the sun is urging the earth to spin faster. More recently E. R. R. Holmberg has gone into this matter more thoroughly, and he finds that while there is an acceleration of the spinning earth because of the atmospheric tides, the actual details proceed in a somewhat different way. Holmberg's value for the accompanying increase in rotational energy is $0.27 \times 10^{19}$ ergs/sec., which may be compared with Jeffreys' figure of $1.1 \times 10^{19}$ ergs/sec. for the rate of energy loss through tidal friction in the ocean.

Tidal friction, and for that matter the electromagnetic braking conjectured by the author, both may very well vary considerably in magnitude. A change in sea level such as is known to have taken place will surely alter the pattern of tidal currents, and any variation in the magnitude or tilting of the earth's magnetic field, again known to have occurred in the past, will affect the induced currents in interplanetary space. The atmospheric tides, however, should not fluctuate appreciably. It is just possible, then, that in the course of geological time the atmospheric acceleration and oceanic deceleration may exactly balance out. Holmberg suggests that this is the case, and that the privitive earth, spinning too fast for atmospheric tides of any size to develop, was slowed down by tidal friction until it reached the magic period of twenty-four hours per turn. Then the sun's influence began to be felt in the atmosphere, billowing it out into tidal bulges which in turn served as a means for pouring rotational energy back into the earth as fast as the ocean tides could drain it out. The current lengthening of the day, if the above picture is correct, is merely a temporary crotchet, and in due course the earth will return to its customary behavior.

The gist of Holmberg's argument is that the twenty-four-hour day is no accident, but is an inevitable consequence of natural laws at work. The more we study Nature the less caprice we find in her doings, a strong point in favor of the above theory.

\* \* \*

Besides the long-period changes in the earth's rotation, there are also variations which last for shorter times but are greater in magnitude. Thus in the past sixty years there have been transient fluctuations in the duration of the day of several thousandths of a second—an immense amount as such things go. However, during this interval the earth has not shifted on its axis by more than 15 feet, which means that whatever agencies are behind the irregular rotation act fairly uniformly around the earth.

The classic discussion of the causes of the short-period changes in the earth's rotation is that given by Walter Munk and Roger Revelle a few years ago. They first considered the possibility that increases and decreases in sea level are responsible; these would alter the moment of inertia of the earth, and so, in order to keep its angular momentum constant, the earth would have to spin slower or faster respectively. (Sea level changes can come about through the melting of Antarctic and/or Greenland ice or the freezing of additional water in those regions.) To account for the observed time variations, though, the sea would have to have dropped about two feet between 1910 and 1930, while the actual figure is only a few inches.

Another idea along the same lines would have the earth's crust undergoing significant changes. The trouble here is, again, that such changes would have to be far greater than are observed. If the immense plateau of Central Asia, including the entire Himalayan range, were to sink to sea level, the length of the day would vary by less than a thousandth of a second. To be sure, if the earth as a whole were irregularly shrinking and expanding by about six inches in radius, everything would be explained—except how the shrinking and expanding come about.

Finally, after discarding a number of other possible mechanisms, Munk and Revelle settled on what appears at first to

81

be a fantastic process. Within the molten metal core of the earth turbulent currents exist—giant eddies and whirlpools writhing far below us. These irregular currents have enough energy associated, with them so that if they are in any way coupled to the mantle of the earth, the observed variations in the earth's rotation can be accounted for. Several investigators have established that an electromagnetic interaction could be acting as the link between core and mantle, in something like the way in which an electromagnet influences pieces of iron near it. The justification for this hypothesis is that the large-scale anomalies in the geomagnetic field are drifting westward very slowly, and nonuniformities in the rate of drift coincide with changes that have occurred in the length of the day. The magnetic anomalies are a consequence of distortions in the electric currents that give rise to the earth's magnetism as a whole, and their westward motion originates in a natural, though complicated, way from internal heating within the core. Turbulence can disrupt the westward motion of the core's electric current system but is not directly able to affect the surrounding mantle. The magnetic paroxysms produced, however, are apparently able to elicit sufficient response from the mantle to affect its rotation. Hardly a self-evident explanation, and not a proved one either, but the most likely yet proposed.

\* \* \*

Until recently the second, the fundamental unit of time in all scientific work, was defined in terms of the length of the day, a somewhat embarrassing situation in view of the irregularities in the earth's rotation. The fundamental units of length and mass (the meter and the kilogram) have simple definitions: they are, respectively, the distance between two scratches on a certain platinum-iridium bar and the mass of a certain platinum-iridium cylinder, both kept at the International Bureau of Weights and Measures at Sèvres, France. Barring catastrophe, these standards are good forever, and even if something should happen to them very precise copies, which have been compared with the originals, exist in many places throughout the world. The basic electrical unit, which has been chosen to be the ampere of current, is defined a little differently, but it too is a fixed, unchanging quantity. The second, though, was tied to the "mean solar day," the average during the year of the time required by the earth to make a complete rotation with reference to the sun. Twenty-four hours of sixty minutes each, with each minute containing sixty seconds, made the second officially 1/86,400 of the mean solar day.

To make the unit of time more trustworthy, it has been changed so that it now refers to the specific year 1900 rather than to the year it finds itself being invoked in. The second is 1/31,556,925.975 of the complete year 1900, and, by comparing astronomical measurements made in that year with current ones, it is possible to convert the present value of the second into its 1900, or Ephemeris, equivalent. An exotic procedure, but a necessary one in this age of exact science.

# SIX

# Terrestrial Magnetism

ALTHOUGH THE EARLIEST DESCRIPTION OF THE COMPASS AND its use in navigation that we have was published by Alexander Neckham in 1180, there is little doubt that knowledge of the compass was widespread even further back in antiquity. Until 1600, however, it was believed that this phenomenon had its origin in an attractive force exerted by Polaris, the North Star, on magnetized needles. In that year, Sir William Gilbert, physician to Elizabeth I, wrote of experiments he had performed with spherical pieces of lodestone, a naturally-magnetized mineral. By comparing the direction of the magnetic force on a test iron needle at various positions near the lodestone sphere with similar measurements made over the earth's surface by explorers, Gilbert concluded that the earth behaves as if it is a giant magnet—*magnus magnes ipse est globus terrestris.*

Today a great deal is known about geomagnetism, and an equally substantial amount is still beyond our grasp. Essentially the information we have is confined to the magnetic field at the earth's surface and a short distance above it. From this information we can deduce that the magnetic field originates within the earth, and that the field must be very strong in the interior. But the big problem of how the field is generated has had only a partial solution so far.

Nearly all of the magnetic field at the earth's surface is equivalent to the field that would be produced by an ordinary bar magnet (or "dipole") of enormous power located a few hundred miles from the center of the earth and tilted by 11° from the direction of the earth's axis (Figure 20). No

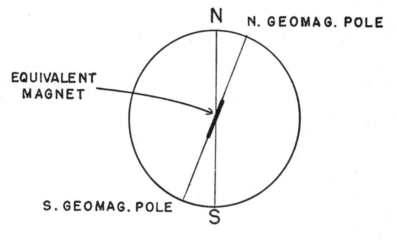

Figure 20.

such magnet can possibly exist, since iron loses its magnetic properties above about 1400° C. and temperatures exceeding this figure are present in all but the top fifteen miles of the earth. However, this dipole is a useful fiction for making computations, and serves as a definite target for theories of the origin of the earth's magnetism to aim at. The points at which the magnetic axis intersects the earth's surface are called the geomagnetic poles and are indicated in Figure 20.

Besides this dipole magnetic field there are irregularities of various kinds also present in the magnetic field of the earth. Some of them are caused by local deposits of iron ore, and magnetic prospecting is a well-developed tool for investigating geological structures as well as for simply looking for iron. Other anomalies come from within the earth, and, in a sense, represent malfunctioning in the operation of the geomagnetic dynamo. The net result is that compasses point to slightly different "magnetic poles" in different regions around the world, and these variations must be indicated on navigation charts. It is true that a spot called a dip pole has been located in each hemisphere at which a compass needle, if suspended freely, would point straight down, and these dip poles are popularly called the "magnetic poles," but since to science the geomagnetic poles are the only important ones, and to the mariner the local direction of the magnetic field is the only important thing, their glamour for explorers is hard to understand.

* * *

Aside from its very existence, the most intriguing aspect of the earth's magnetism lies in the changes it has experienced in the past. That such changes occur was discovered quite early in the game, when Henry Gellibrand noticed in 1634 that the direction to which a compass needle pointed in London seemed to vary from year to year. From 1576, the earliest date for which appropriate records exist, a compass in London would have gone from 8° east of true north all the way over to 24° west in 1823, whereupon it would have begun meandering back until now it is about 8° west. Magnetic records for Paris, starting in 1617, exhibit similar wandering. From these data it would seem that the geomagnetic axis is moving around within the earth so that it makes a complete circle in about five hundred years, but when records for other parts of the globe are examined this conclusion is less attractive; such compass variations are more likely local affairs and are not shared by the entire planet.

The strength of the geomagnetic field itself has been measured for over a century, and in that period has dropped by about 6 per cent. This decrease is definitely not a local anomaly, since the measurements from which it is derived were obtained all over the world. The immediate conclusion that we can draw is that the field must originate in the liquid core, where physical changes can take place rapidly (a century is a very brief interval on a geological time scale), and not in the mantle, whose solid nature inhibits any but long-term phenomena. While this does no more than reinforce our assumption that the earth's magnetism arises in the core owing to the possibility of electric currents there, it is comforting to have such corroboration.

\* \* \*

Quite apart from these small but precisely-known magnetic variations of the recent past, evidence has been found for changes of a spectacular nature that occurred much further back in the history of the earth.

From the earliest times it has been known that certain rocks are naturally magnetized, but only recently has it been possible to interpret the data so as to yield information on the magnetic field that existed when and where they were formed. In studying fossil magnetism the procedure is to cut a specimen from a geological formation of known age, marking its orientation, and then, in the laboratory, to determine the direction in which it is magnetized. By comparing this direction with the orientation the specimen had in its parent rock, the local direction of the geomagnetic field (that is, the direction in which a compass needle would point) at the time the rock was formed can be found. And these directions often differ considerably from the direction of the present magnetic field.

Before we go into the results of the experiments with fossil magnetism, we must make note of the many difficulties and ambiguities present. For one thing, the geological structure from which a sample is taken may have shifted its position since it was formed—tilting and folding, for instance, are rather commonly encountered. For another, in the case of sedimentary rocks and clays which were formed by the gradual deposition of finely divided material, the alignment of the magnetized particles may have been influenced more by mechanical than magnetic forces. By taking sufficient pains, however, effects of this kind can be taken into account. More difficult to deal with are magnetically unstable rocks, not always easy to recognize, whose magnetizations may not be representative of the period in which they were formed.

Primary in the interpretation of fossil magnetism is the hypothesis that the geomagnetic and geographic poles have never been far apart. From a theoretical standpoint, as we shall see, this is a necessary consequence of the generation of the magnetic field in the liquid core; experimentally, there are indications that the present 11½° angle between the geomagnetic axis and the rotational axis is unusually large, and that this angle has averaged half this amount or less in the past.

Going on the assumption that the geomagnetic and geographic poles have always roughly coincided, the fossil magnetism studies show that the earth's crust has shifted radically with respect to its interior. When we discussed problems of world climate, we saw how convenient polar wandering of this kind would be for interpreting the glaciation of India, Australia, South Africa, and South America that occurred 200 million years ago, contemporaneous with an almost tropical climate in North America and China. Polar wandering perhaps involves a smaller stretching of the scientific imagination than Wegener's continental drift, but climatic considerations alone, while strong, were not conclusive enough for the idea to be regarded as established. The fossil magnetic data seem on the way to doing just this.

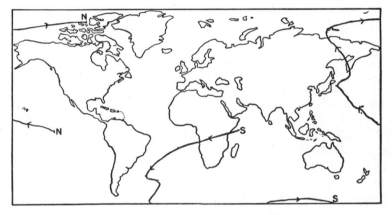

Figure 21.

Figure 21 is a map of the world showing the tracks made by the North and South poles in the past 500 million years. In Pre-Cambrian times the North Pole was somewhere in mid-Pacific and from there migrated via Japan and Siberia to its present position; the South Pole, meanwhile, moved across Africa and down the South Atlantic Ocean. We must beware of taking this particular map too seriously, but, since climatic

89

and magnetic data independently point to polar wandering of the kind shown, it must be somewhere near the truth.

\* \* \*

The same techniques used to measure fossil magnetism can be applied to less ancient materials. Thus kiln walls in the ruins of Carthage are found to be slightly magnetized, and the direction and intensity of magnetization represent the same parameters of the geomagnetic field at Carthage at the time of its downfall. The reason for this inference is that all substances lose their magnetization when strongly heated; the kilns of Carthage were presumably firing pottery until near the end, and the remnant magnetization must therefore date from then. The pottery of early civilizations yields information on the dip of the local magnetic field relative to the horizontal, although it cannot, of course, reveal the direction of the field in the horizontal (since we have no way of knowing which way the vases and bowls were standing when they were fired other than that they were vertical).

What has been determined about the geomagnetic field in the past few thousand years is not as glamorous as the methods used to obtain it, for it appears that there has not been very much change. There are indications that in Roman times the field was half again as large as it is now, which agrees with the gradual decrease noted in the last hundred years although the latter represents a more rapid rate. Further, a detailed study by the author based on the carbon 14 dating of archeological specimens shows that the geomagnetic field cannot have changed much in the past 15,000 years or so. This conclusion was obtained in the circuitous manner characteristic of much of geophysics. Neutrons produced in the upper atmosphere by cosmic rays are captured by the nuclei of nitrogen atoms, which thereupon are converted into radioactive carbon 14. Thus a small proportion of all of the carbon on the earth is radioactive, and is continually being ingested by living things. When a plant or animal dies, it ceases to take in additional carbon 14, and the radioactivity in its body decreases with time. By comparing the relative concentrations of carbon 14 in living and dead specimens, then, the time that has elapsed since the latter's death can be determined. The half-life of carbon 14 is about 6000 years; a tree which died 6000 years ago will exhibit half the radioactivity of a tree presently alive.

Now cosmic rays reaching the earth are affected by the earth's magnetic field, which acts as a kind of umbrella to deflect the weaker cosmic rays from everywhere but the polar regions. If the field were smaller, more cosmic rays would reach the atmosphere, while if it were greater, fewer cosmic rays would get in. In the event of either of these changes the rate of carbon 14 production would change, and the basis for using carbon 14 as a clock for the past would disappear. But carbon 14 dates and dates obtained in other ways (for instance by tree-ring counts) agree in the main, implying that the average cosmic ray intensity, and the average geomagnetic field strength, have not varied by very much in the period (15,000 years) covered, although small fluctuations may have taken place.

*  *  *

The real *pièce de résistance* of fossil magnetism is the discovery that the earth's magnetic field has reversed itself innumerable times. In numerous locations rock specimens of different ages exhibit opposite magnetic polarities, and it seemed that the only explanation was that the earth's field had reversed itself more than once during the period of formation of the various rocks. Then it was pointed out that there were at least four different mechanisms by which a magnetized rock could spontaneously reverse the direction of its magnetization. For some time there was nothing but confusion, but after a while it became apparent that the original conclusion was still correct: the field *has* reversed itself some thousands of times in geological history, although not all of the evidence pointing to this fact can be accepted as legitimate.

These reversals do not represent an incessant sliding of the earth's crust over the mantle. Instead, each time the geomagnetic field probably dropped to zero in a period of several thousand years, and shortly was resurrected with the opposite polarity. Then, after a longer interval of from a hundred thousand to a few million years, the field reversed itself once more. Apparently these flip-flops are a regular feature of the dynamo within the earth's core, and represent one more problem for those who have the temerity to try to explain such a dynamo.

\* \* \*

Finally we come to the origin of the earth's magnetism. The most successful approach, in which the prime movers have been Sir Edward Bullard in England and Walter Elsasser here, is based upon the relatively new science of hydromagnetism. (New as it is, it has already undergone a change of name from the more cumbersome magnetohydrodynamics.) We must not be fooled into thinking that magnetic water is involved; rather, hydromagnetism treats of the interactions between magnetic and fluid dynamic effects, interactions that take place only in gases and liquids which are good conductors of electricity. Accordingly, hydromagnetism is principally concerned with such astrophysical phenomena as sunspots and galactic structure, but finds application also in the liquid iron core of the earth. (We might remark, as an aside, that hydromagnetic principles are being applied to the generation of thermonuclear power, which, when perfected, will represent almost as great a jump in technology as the first utilization of fire.)

Let us begin at the beginning. One of the basic principles of physics is that all magnetic fields arise from electric currents. Conversely, all currents are surrounded by magnetic fields. When a coil of wire that is free to rotate is placed in a magnetic field, passing the proper current through it will cause its resultant magnetic field and the external magnetic field to exert forces on one another so as to turn the coil. This is the mechanism behind the electric motor, which operates through the medium of magnetic forces.

There is also a reciprocal effect: when a wire or other conductor of electricity is subjected to a changing magnetic field, a current is induced in it. If we move a wire in a magnetic field, then, we have a generator of electric current.

Now let us connect an electric motor and a generator together, electrically and mechanically. At first glance it appears that the combination will go on forever, once we have given it an initial push, with the generator supplying power to the motor which in turn rotates the generator to produce more power. Unfortunately this cannot be the case, owing to the inevitable presence of friction, resistance in the connecting wires, and similar agencies of power loss. However, given a small external energy source sufficient to make up the power dissipated to friction and such, there is no reason why the motor-generator should not continue indefinitely. And, in the vicinity of the combination, we will encounter a magnetic field that results from the various currents that are flowing.

In essence most theories of the earth's magnetism invoke a mechanism of this kind, in which there is a coupling between mechanical, electrical, and magnetic phenomena. The

93

required auxiliary energy is presumably supplied by the solid central core in the form of heat, which then produces convective motions in the liquid iron. There is no agreement on the manner in which the heat itself is produced; some authorities feel that it comes from radioactive materials there, while others plump for chemical processes and crystallization as the answer. In any event the required heat is not large, and no one doubts that enough is present.

Nor is there any trouble about the initial push which must be given the dynamo to start it running. In any electrically conducting fluid in which irregular motions are present there is certain to occur, sooner or later, a fugitive current, and its magnetic field, which must change either in relative direction or magnitude owing to the fluid motions, in turn induces other currents in the surrounding fluid. These currents possess their own magnetic fields, which again with the help of the fluid motions lead to other fields. The problem is not to account for the existence of terrestrial magnetism, which indeed cannot help arising in the core, but to explain why it leads to an external field virtually identical with that of a simple bar magnet.

The materials the theorist has at his command, then, consist of a spherical container filled with liquid iron. The container has a solid core which is warmer than the iron, and so convective currents are set up which transport the heat outward and stir up the iron as well. In addition, the entire container is rotating, which serves to deflect the fluid currents to their right in the northern hemisphere and to their left in the southern. (A familiar analog of this effect, known as the Coriolis acceleration, is the counterclockwise pattern of hurricane winds in the northern hemisphere and the clockwise pattern in the southern.) Given a small, random fragment of magnetic field, why does this spinning bottle of liquid iron amplify it so exactly into the regular field that we find at the earth's surface?

* * *

Before we attempt to answer this question, let us admit that it paints a more gloomy picture than is warranted. As it happens, the magnetic field observed at some distance from any system of electric currents, no matter how simple or complex, can be described in terms of combinations of bar magnets. The more elaborate the field, the more bar magnets we need to describe it, each of a different strength and oriented in a different direction. That portion of the field which can be described by a single bar magnet is called the dipole part; of the remainder, some can be described by pairs of identical bar magnets in one or more of several arrangements, and is called the quadrupole part; some of the field that is still left might require four identical bar magnets in a particular configuration to duplicate it, and is the octupole part; and so on. The characteristic thing about this way of looking at a complicated magnetic field is that we can use the known behavior of the fields of bar magnets in combination to trace the actual field at various distances from its source. The dipole part of the field diminishes only gradually in strength with distance while the quadrupole part drops more rapidly and the octupole part more rapidly still. The higher "order" field components go down in intensity so fast as we go away from the currents that give rise to them that they may be almost imperceptible only a moderate distance out.

At the earth's surface, as we noted earlier in this chapter, the predominant part of the magnetic field is that of a dipole. There are, however, small irregularities which represent more complex field elements such as might be produced by quadrupoles, octupoles, and so forth. When we pursue these higher-order components back to the core, they become more intense at a faster rate than the simple dipole. At the core, as calculation shows, the irregular part of the surface field is just as strong as the regular dipole part; the only reason it is minor at the surface is its limited reach. Thus the field that we must account for is not an elegant, pure dipole at all, but rather a more or less mixed-up magnetic field whose chief sign of order is that its dipole component tends to stay aligned along the rotational axis of the earth.

\*   \*   \*

The chain of events in the core that lead to the observed geomagnetic field seems to be something like the following. Magnetic lines of force that exist initially are dragged around by the fluid motion so that they form closed loops, like parallels of latitude. These loops cannot be detected outside of the core, but are believed to be very numerous within it. It is in the formation of the loops that energy is fed into the magnetic field, since work must be done by the fluid motions in the core in stretching the original lines of force into their new shapes. Portions of the loops are then twisted by combined convection and Coriolis acceleration into smaller loops which lie in meridional planes (a meridional plane corresponds to a thin orange segment). These loops then coalesce into the dipole—or bar magnet—field we perceive at the earth's surface, and the cycle starts over.

Of course, the true picture is much more involved, but at least the mechanism described can take care of the main features of the observed field. There is no difficulty in explaining the alignment of the magnetic and rotational axes, since the symmetry of motion imposed by the spinning earth must be reflected in the field generated as a result of the spin.

Further, reversals in the external dipole field can occur as a result of changes in the pattern of fluid currents in the core. And, most important, the feedback between the two systems of lines of force, the dipole and the internal closed loops, is self-regulating, so that the external field remains fairly constant in the intervals between reversals.

At the present time, then, the theory of the earth's magnetism is essentially a silhouette, providing a suggestive outline but leaving the details in the shadow. Scarcely a satisfactory theory, but, like Dr. Johnson's lady preacher, to be marveled at for merely existing.

# SEVEN

# The Origin of the Earth

THE TITLE OF THIS CHAPTER IS A RATHER PRESUMPTUOUS ONE, because we will never know with any certainty how the solar system came into being. Not only was nobody there at the time, but also planets are too minute (on an astronomical scale) for us to detect them in, perhaps, various stages of their evolution near stars other than the sun. Still, there is much about the birth of the solar system that we can infer from what we know of the laws of nature and the observed facts of stellar life. The results, while not so much a single universally accepted theory as a group of different hypotheses, sharing certain conclusions and conflicting among themselves on others, nevertheless allow us to sketch in a rough way the origin of the earth and its fellow planets with some assurance that we are at least on the right track.

\*    \*    \*

We have already alluded a number of times to something called angular momentum, on each occasion defining it in a rather loose fashion. We can no longer regard it so casually, because the extraordinary distribution of angular momentum between the sun and planets has proved to be one of the chief obstacles in the way of an explanation for the origin of the solar system.

What precisely *is* angular momentum? Just as ordinary momentum is a measure of the tendency of a moving body to keep on moving in the same direction with the same velocity, angular momentum is a measure of the tendency of a rotating body to continue rotating. Further, all bodies traveling in curved paths possess angular momentum, so that the earth, for example, has a certain amount of angular momentum associated with its daily rotation on its axis plus an additional amount associated with its annual revolution about the sun. A force must be applied in order to provide an object with linear momentum, and similarly a torque (or twist) is required for the acquisition of the angular momentum. Whatever mechanism was involved in the formation of the solar system must therefore have been capable of having imparted to the various bodies that compose it the angular momentum they now have.

The latter statement is innocuous enough as it stands until we proceed to compute the angular momenta in the solar system. We begin with the sun, which makes a complete rotation in a little more than twenty-five days. Its angular momentum is $1.6 \times 10^{48}$ g cm$^2$/sec. Then we add up the angular momenta of the planets and their satellites: the total is $3.15 \times 10^{50}$ g cm$^2$/sec. This means that the sun has only 2 per cent of the angular momentum of the solar system as a whole. But the sun's mass is $2 \times 10^{33}$ g, as compared with the $2.7 \times 10^{30}$ g total mass of the planets, satellites, and asteroids. Thus the planetary system, with $1/750$ of the mass of the sun, has fifty times more angular momentum!

\* \* \*

In a way it is difficult, without actually performing calculations of an esoteric nature, to appreciate the audacity of the solar system in assuming so inside-out a dynamical arrangement. Let us look into some theories of solar system origin to see its importance.

The earliest theories of planetary origin, proposed in the eighteenth century by Kant and Laplace, both began with the sun inside a rotating gaseous nebula. According to Kant the nebula flattened out as a result of collisions taking place between the particles composing it, and the ring that was formed then condensed into what are now the planets. Laplace had the nebula contract into the sun, which, with the additional angular momentum of the nebular material, began spinning rapidly—so rapidly that, according to Laplace, rings of matter split off from the solar equator because of the centrifugal force, with each ring subsequently condensing to form a planet. Satellite genesis came about in a similar manner. Both Kant's and Laplace's hypotheses seem like reasonable starting points for detailed work; but alas, both are helpless to account for the angular momentum of the planets.

As the crucial nature of the angular momentum problem became evident, it seemed that the only way out was to postulate a cataclysmic beginning for the solar system. In the early years of this century Chamberlin and Moulton proposed that another star came close to the sun in the remote past, plucking out by gravitational attraction a huge gob of solar material. The latter was then given angular momentum through the torque exerted on it by the now receding star, and later condensed into discrete planets. Jeffreys criticized the whole idea on the ground that planets could not form from the ejected solar matter, and instead suggested that the passing star drew out a long, cigar-shaped wisp from the primitive sun. This wisp was unstable and broke up into the various planets, which obtained their angular momentum from debris striking them after itself having gained angular momentum from the visiting star.

Jeffreys' idea proved unable upon closer inspection to satisfy the requirements of the angular momentum distribution. He then put forward a revised version, in which an actual collision occurred between the sun and another star. This could not have been a head-on collision, or the angular momentum difficulty would remain, but must have been more of a grazing encounter. The two stars would have spun about one another before separating, so that the material emitted by them that stayed near the sun would be whirling rapidly. From this material condensation into planets then occurred.

Some years after the new theory of Jeffreys was proposed, H. N. Russell pointed out that, while it could take care of the axial angular momentum caused by rotation, it failed miserably for the orbital angular momentum of the outer planets about the sun. The reason for this failure is the immense distances of these planets from the sun as compared with the separation of the sun and the colliding star: Neptune, for instance, is 500 times farther out than the star would have been at its nearest point of approach. To remedy the situation, Russell had the sun initially accompanied by a smaller companion star. The convenient passing star then smashed up the companion, leaving behind the ancestral material of the planets while taking the rest of the wreckage along with it. (Note the extremity to which it seemed necessary to go in order to provide the requisite angular momentum to the planets.) Unfortunately even this extreme scheme will not do, since in the course of such a collision most of the ejected material would escape while the rest would form a diffuse gas cloud around the surviving stars.

Other—many other—origins for the solar system have been

proposed having at their hearts catastrophic events of some sort, but all have failed, either because they could not get past the hurdle of angular momentum or because in doing so they managed to get tripped up by their exertions. However the world will end, it almost surely began not with a bang.

*   *   *

Theories of the origin of the solar system that involve gradual processes such as might reasonably have occurred at some point in the evolution of the sun offer more promise than the more spectacular collision hypotheses. Before going into them, though, we must pause and inquire into the age of the earth and the amount of time that was available for its formation. A remarkable number of different methods for determining these time scales have been devised, and we shall try to indicate the most significant ones.

The first serious try at calculating the data of the Creation was made by Bishop Ussher of the Church of England in the middle of the seventeenth century. This celebrated feat was based on the chronological material in the Old Testament, from which Ussher reckoned that the Earth and the Firmament came into being in 4004 B.C. His scholarly *Annales Veteris et Novi Testamenti* was accepted as impeccable by no less than Isaac Newton, who was no mean Biblical chronologist himself. Later research was able to pin down the moment of Creation more precisely: 9:00 A.M., October 23, 4004 B.C. Alas, transports of intellect, unlike those of ecstasy, cannot speed the sands of time, and it now appears that Ussher was in error by some billions of years.

Other schemes of similar scientific merit for determining the age of the earth have been applauded in the past, but we shall pass over them since the current crop is just as imaginative and probably more accurate.

Let us start with the fact that our sun, together with its halo of planets, is presently coursing through the heavens at a speed of about 12 miles per second. Since there are plenty of stars in these heavens, even though they are not particularly close to us, there is a certain definite probability that, given enough time, the sun will pass near enough to one of them for some disturbance to occur in the solar system. The "enough time" is something like 1000 billion years. But no such encounter between the sun and an astronomical body of substantial size has yet taken place. The evidence for this flat statement is the shape of Neptune's orbit, which is very close to being a perfect circle. If the solar system had ever passed through the neighborhood of another star, this circle would unquestionably have been distorted into an ellipse, if indeed it could have avoided complete disruption. The fact that most of the other planetary orbits deviate somewhat from a circular shape is not evidence in favor of a stellar meeting, because any number of effects arising within the solar system could produce such irregularities; but the symmetry of Neptune's path is an excellent argument against a stellar meeting in which the sun participated. The conclusion, then is that the solar system must be younger than 1000 billion years, although how much younger we cannot tell from this line of reasoning.

Another upper limit can be found by examining the life cycles of stars. Stars begin as clouds of gas and dust that condense from diffuse interstellar matter, and in their childhood and youth are largely composed of hydrogen. The energy they emit as light and heat comes from the gradual conversion of their hydrogen content into helium. This process can occur in two different ways. In the sun and other stars of its size and smaller, the helium is formed more or less directly: two hydrogen atoms collide, and their nuclei (which are protons) stick together, forming a "deuteron" with the

103

emission of a positive electron and a neutrino; then another hydrogen atom strikes the deuteron some time later, and its nucleus happens to stick, this time with the emission of a gamma ray. Finally two of these combinations come across one another and adhere, forming a helium atom and discarding the two protons which are left over. This series of nuclear reactions takes an average about three billion years from start to finish, but in stars there are so many atoms in various stages of the process that helium is being formed essentially in a continuous manner.

In larger and hotter stars than the sun, the conversion of hydrogen to helium takes place with the help of carbon. A carbon atom catches four protons in succession, each time being converted into a different form, and finally disgorges a complete helium atom while returning to its original state. The period of the carbon cycle is about six million years. In both processes, the key to the energy production is that the final helium atom weight is *less* than the total weight of the four hydrogen atoms that went into making it. The missing mass is converted to energy according to the Einstein formula $E = mc^2$, and accounts for the radiation from stars.

The formation of helium takes place in the interior of a star where the pressure is sufficiently great for the various reactants to come together reasonably often. Ultimately all the interior hydrogen will be used up, and the "fire" will spread outward in the star in order to use up the hydrogen there. As this happens the star will expand and grow more and more luminous, becoming what is known as a red giant. (When our sun goes into this phase some four or five billions of years hence, it is estimated that it will swell up until its diameter is that of the orbit of Venus.) Then in its old age the star will proceed to shrink down, obtaining energy by the inefficient process of three helium atoms simultaneously colliding to form a carbon atom. After a while there will be enough carbon for the reaction involving a carbon atom and a helium atom to occur, with the production of oxygen and the emission of energy. Ultimately heavier and heavier atoms are built up, until, nearing senility, the star is racked by convulsions of various kinds, perhaps even culminating, some astronomers believe, in a vast explosion that is visible as a supernova. The remains of the star then give up the ghost and collapse into what is known as a white dwarf, a small but very dense body with no future to speak of.

What has all of this to do with the age of the earth? The answer appears when we learn that there are two different types of star groups. In the midst of Population I groups there is still plenty of interstellar material, from which new stars are being born continually. In Population II groups, however, all the interstellar material seems to have been used up at once, and no new stars are being created.

Thus Population II stars, which in our galaxy are in the form of globular clusters, are all of the same age. From the characteristics of the light emitted by stars, astronomers can infer the stage their life cycles are in, though this by itself does not help since large stars evolve more rapidly than small ones. However, since all the Population II stars in a particular globular cluster originated at the same time, by determining the numbers of the various stellar phases that remain it is possible to infer the age of the cluster. In our galaxy the globular clusters are up to six and a half billion years old; the sun, owing to its position near the galactic rim, is probably younger, so that the upper limit to its age—and therefore to the age of the earth—is, say, six billion years.

\*　\*　\*

Now let us approach the age of the earth from the other end, so to speak, and examine terrestrial processes that might

105

give hints as to the minimum time the earth must have existed.

One method of interest concerns the rate at which the rivers and streams of the world erode the land through which they pass and deposit the resulting sediment in the oceans. About one-fifth of a cubic mile of sediment is carried away each year, and the ocean bottom now contains some $7 \times 10^7$ cubic miles of it. Dividing yields a time of a third of a billion years. However, as we have seen, the face of the earth and the height of the sea have changed both often and radically in the past, so an estimate based on present figures for the production of sediment is not particularly reliable, though interesting.

Another lower limit comes from the ages of rocks. These can be determined by virtue of their content of radioactive materials which, in the course of time, decay at a constant rate. Thus radium decays into the gas radon in such a way that half of an original sample is transformed in 1622 years, half of the remainder in the next 1622 years, and so on. If radon were stable and could be collected, by comparing the amount of radium left from a sample with the amount of radon produced, the time the experiment was begun could be calculated. For our purposes radium is not very good, since its own half-life is short compared with the age of the earth. The radioactive materials most useful for dating rocks are uranium 238, which decays through a chain of daughter products into lead 206 in $4\frac{1}{2}$ billion years; uranium 235, whose decay through its own chain of daughter products into lead 207 requires 700 million years, and thorium 232, whose decay into lead 208, again via daughter radioactive atoms, involves 14 billion years. In all these decay chains one of the atoms is that of a gas, and if it escapes before being transformed into an atom that will remain in the rock the dating method fails. However, a number of rock types exist whose

106

structure is sufficiently impermeable for reasonable success.

There are several methods for finding the age of a given rock from its content of radioactive materials and their decay products. One is to compare the quantity of a lead isotope present with the quantity of one of the preceding members of the radioactive series of which it is the end product. Another makes use of the fact that uranium 235 and uranium 238 are always found together in a certain specific relative abundance. Since they decay at different rates, a comparison of the abundances of lead 206 and lead 207 with the relative abundances of their parents uranium 238 and uranium 235 gives the age of the sample.

The difficulty with the above methods is that they require a means for distinguishing between different lead isotopes, which are identical chemically but have slightly different atomic weights. Until recently this could not be done, and, because there is plenty of ordinary lead 204 around which has no radioactive origin, a simple comparison between the amount of lead in a rock and the amount of uranium there is meaningless. However, during the radioactive decays of the elements we are concerned with, helium is emitted, and if it is efficiently trapped in the rock in which it is formed a comparison of its amount with that of the parent radioactive material yields the age of the rock. (For example, in the course of its decay an atom of thorium produces six atoms of helium.) The big trouble here is that helium escapes readily, and even in the most cooperative rocks some is bound to have gotten out in the billion or more years since it was formed.

Today rock dating is a well-developed profession, and a large number of samples of various kinds have been processed. The oldest known rocks solidified 2.7 billion years ago, but this is only a lower limit to the age of the earth's crust since the rocks may well have been melted one or more times since its formation. As a matter of fact, these rocks were found embedded in sedimentary rocks in such a way that it was apparent that the latter were present first; hence the 2.7 billion years is a minimum even neglecting crustal remelting.

\* \* \*

We have examined two methods each for setting upper and lower limits to the earth's age, which turns out to lie between 2.7 and 6 billion years. There are still other techniques up the geophysicist's sleeve for obtaining an even more precise figure. By itself, each is not too reliable, but since they are quite independent and agree among themselves very well, we are justified in assigning significance to the time that emerges.

One elegant approach is to date meteorites, which presumably were formed at about the same time as the rest of the solar system. This can be done by radioactive methods, and the result is an age of about 4½ billion years from the time the meteorites solidified.

Another tack concerns the moon and the effect of the earth's tides in speeding up its motion. Under the action of the tides, the moon has been drawing away from the earth. Let us project backward the present rate of lunar recession. When this is done we find that about 4 billion years ago the earth and moon were close together, which would have been a necessary consequence of a common origin of these bodies. To be sure, sea level and therefore tidal effects have varied in the earth's history and so we must not be too dogmatic about the calculation of the earth's age on this basis, but it is nice to find the figure 4 billion years again.

A further indication of the earth's age is provided by the presence of the gas argon in the atmosphere. Virtually all the argon in the universe has mass numbers of 36 or 38, and exists in only minor amounts. On the earth, however, argon constitutes about 1 per cent of the lower atmosphere, and the argon 40 isotope is preponderant. There is not only too much argon, but it is the wrong kind.

The German physicist von Weizsäcker came to the rescue with the suggestion—later verified—that argon 40 could be produced by the radioactive decay of potassium 40. There is only one part of potassium 40 in ten thousand parts of ordinary potassium, and potassium 40 decays into calcium 40 ten times as often as it decays into argon 40, but there is so much potassium around that there is enough argon 40 production to account for its abundance on the earth. Putting it in numbers, we find once more about 4½ billion years for the age of the earth.

The bulk of the evidence, then, points toward 4½ billion years as the most likely figure. We must keep in mind that this age refers to the time the earth solidified and assumed its present general character. Since the universe came into being about 6 billion years ago, as revealed by observations of the expanding universe as well as by the stellar evolution studies already mentioned, this leaves a period of a billion and a half years from the origin of the universe for the formation of the earth.

\* \* \*

The ideas of planetary genesis that are most widely accepted today began with a discussion by Carl von Weizsäcker in 1944. He stressed considerations based on fluid dynamics, which made it possible to understand, for the first time, how the condensation processes that produced the planets led to Bode's law and to the observed distribution of angular momentum. The arguments of von Weizsäcker were subject to criticism on various grounds, but subsequent work, largely by G. P. Kuiper, has led to what appears to be a plausible enough picture.

The story begins with a local eddy in the swirling gas of the primoridal galaxy. This eddy in time condensed into a cloud stable enough to resist disruption. The cloud, the so-called protosun, was as far across as the present solar system, and had a considerable amount of angular momentum. It then began to contract, taking 80 million years to make the transition from gas cloud to star. In the course of the contraction some of the gas—about 10 per cent—remained behind to form a diffuse spherical nebula about the nascent sun.

In time the nebula cooled and flattened into a thin disc. In doing so its density increased, and ultimately reached the point at which mutual gravitational forces within the disc became as great as the differential gravitational forces exerted by the sun. (The latter are of the same kind as the differential tide-producing forces caused by the moon that were described earlier.) This created an unstable situation, which resolved itself when the flattened nebula broke up into separate smaller clouds. These were the protoplanets from which the planets of the present developed. Had the nebular density been less than it was, according to Kuiper, many tiny planets would have resulted, while if it had been much greater one or more small stars would have been formed as companions to the sun.

While the protoplanets were coming into existence the sun was still dark, not yet having completed the shrinkage that would permit it to evolve energy and become luminous. The protoplanets were huge affairs, protoearth, for instance, being 500 times heavier and 2000 times as far across as the current earth. With the sun in darkness the heavier constituents of the protoplanets migrated inward, collecting in the center of each protoplanet to form a heavy core surrounded by lighter gases. At this time the satellites got their start. In the case of protoearth, for some reason, only a single large secondary body developed, so large, in fact, that the earth and moon must properly be regarded as a double planet.

Then the sun began to shine, and the peaceful evolution of the protoplanets reached a more dramatic phase. In addition to the light it emits, the sun puts out an intense flux of fast, ionized particles. Today these particles lead to auroral displays and magnetic disturbances on the earth and the deflection of comet tails away from the sun, among other effects; during the early stages of planetary evolution they served to sweep the solar system free of the remnant nebular gas that pervaded interplanetary space. Meanwhile the cold protoplanets grew warm, and their own envelopes of gas and vapor began to boil away. The earth and the other planets nearest the sun suffered an immense dimunition in their sizes and weights, since the light hydrogen and helium of which they were largely composed could escape easily. Finally, after the greater part of a billion years, the relatively bare, shrunken planets of today emerged permanently from the mists that enshrouded them.

Meanwhile the protoplanet cores were proceeding to consolidate themselves. In the case of the earth this led to pronounced heating, resulting partly from the conversion of gravitational potential energy to thermal energy during contraction and partly to radioactivity. Ultimately the entire earth melted, and the iron and silicate components separated to form the core and mantle respectively. Then, gravitational energy exhausted, the molten earth began to solidify, and with the development of the crust and its continents, a recognizable ancestor of our present planet appeared. As we saw, this happened $4\frac{1}{2}$ billion years ago, completing a process that had begun a billion or so years earlier.

\* \* \*

In a way we have a better idea of the future course of the earth than we have of its past. In the next few billion years the sun will swell into a luminous giant, as large around as the orbit of Venus and emitting a hundred times more radiation than it does now. The earth will grow warmer, and ultimately the oceans will reach the boiling point. Steam will fill the atmosphere, and all life will perish except, conceivably, some exceedingly resistant spores. This situation will last perhaps a billion years, until the sun begins to decline in the evolutionary process that will end with it a feeble white dwarf. The steam will condense into new oceans as the earth cools, terminating in a globe completely covered with ice and snow. Doubtless a little volcanic activity will still persist, but the ultimate picture will be one of lifeless desolation as permanent darkness draws near.

# Appendix

## SOME PROPERTIES OF THE EARTH

| | |
|---|---|
| Equatorial radius | 3963.34 miles |
| Polar radius | 3949.99 miles |
| Radius if a perfect sphere | 3958.89 miles |
| Circumference at equator | 24,902 miles |
| Weight | $6.595 \times 10^{21}$ tons |
| Average density | 345 lb./cubic foot |
| Surface area | 196,940,000 square miles |
| Land area | 56,222,000 square miles |
| Water area | 140,718,000 square miles |
| Average speed in orbit | 18.5 miles/second |
| Speed of rotation at equator | 0.29 miles/second |
| Velocity of sun relative to nearby stars | 12.05 miles/second |
| Velocity of sun relative to center of galaxy | 136 miles/second |

## SOME PROPERTIES OF THE MOON AND PLANETS

| BODY | MASS (EARTH = 1) | RADIUS (EARTH = 1) | PERIOD OF ROTATION (DAYS) | DENSITY (WATER = 1) | SURFACE GRAVITY (EARTH = 1) | TEMPERATURE (°F.) | SATELLITES |
|---|---|---|---|---|---|---|---|
| Mercury | 0.054 | 0.38 | 88 | 5.46 | 0.38 | light side 780° | 0 |
| Venus | 0.814 | 0.967 | 15–30 | 4.96 | 0.87 | dark side −9° light side 135° | 0 |
| Earth | 1.000 | 1.000 | 1.00 | 5.52 | 1.00 | mean 57° | 1 |
| Mars | 0.107 | 0.523 | 1.03 | 4.12 | 0.39 | warmest part 54° | 2 |
| Jupiter | 318 | 10.97 | 0.41 | 1.33 | 2.65 | −36° | 12 |
| Saturn | 95.3 | 9.03 | 0.43 | 0.71 | 1.17 | −225° | 9 |
| Uranus | 14.6 | 3.72 | 0.45 | 1.56 | 1.05 | −300° | 5 |
| Neptune | 17.3 | 3.38 | 0.66 | 2.47 | 1.23 | ? | 2 |
| Pluto | 0.1 | 0.45 | ? | 5.5 | 0.5 | ? | 0 |
| Moon | 0.012 | 0.273 | 27.3 | 3.33 | 0.16 | light side 260° | |

## SOME PROPERTIES OF THE SOLAR SYSTEM

| BODY | MEAN DISTANCE FROM SUN | MEAN ORBITAL VELOCITY | LENGTH OF YEAR * |
|------|------------------------|------------------------|-------------------|
| Mercury | 36 million miles | 30 miles/sec | 88 days |
| Venus | 67 | 22 | 225 |
| Earth | 93 | 18 | 365 |
| Mars | 142 | 13 | 687 |
| Jupiter | 483 | 8.1 | 4,333 |
| Saturn | 886 | 6.0 | 10,759 |
| Uranus | 1,783 | 4.2 | 30,687 |
| Neptune | 2,793 | 3.4 | 60,184 |
| Pluto | 3,666 | 2.9 | 90,700 |

* Period of revolution around the sun measured in terms of the length of the earth's day.

# Index

# Index

# INDEX